AN EXHIBITION OF SCROLLS AND ARCHAEOLOGICAL ARTIFACTS FROM THE COLLECTIONS OF THE ISRAEL ANTIQUITIES AUTHORITY

AYALA SUSSMANN AND RUTH PELED

LIBRARY OF CONGRESS · WASHINGTON · 1993

IN ASSOCIATION WITH

THE ISRAEL ANTIQUITIES AUTHORITY

THE FIELD MUSEUM · CHICAGO · 2000

SCROLLS FROM THE DEAD SEA

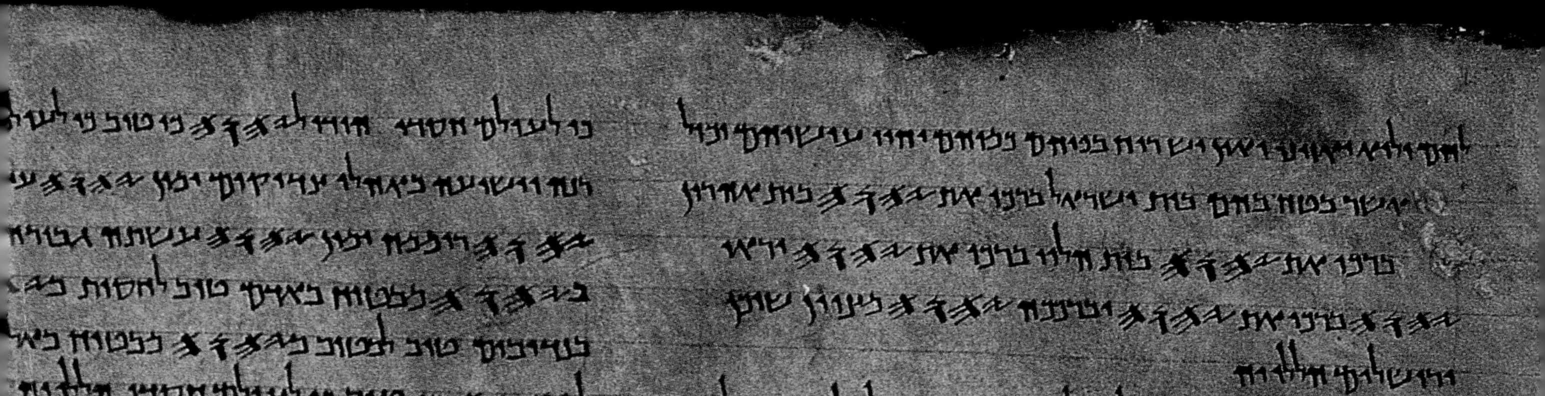

Revised edition published in 2000 by

THE FIELD MUSEUM
1400 South Lake Shore Drive
Chicago, Illinois 60605-2496
312-922-9410
www.fieldmuseum.org

LIBRARY OF CONGRESS CATALOGING-IN-PUBLICATION DATA

Scrolls from the Dead Sea : an exhibition of scrolls and archaeological artifacts from the col-
    lections of the Israel Antiquities Authority / [edited by] Ayala Sussmann and Ruth Peled.
        p.   cm.
    Catalog issued in conjunction with an exhibition held at the Library of Congress,
    Apr. 29–Aug. 1, 1993; New York Public Library, Oct. 2, 1993–Jan. 8, 1994; M. H. de Young
    Memorial Museum, Feb. 26–May 8, 1994; Field Museum, March 10–June 11, 2000.
    Includes facsimiles of selected texts with English translation.
    Includes bibliographical references and index.
    ISBN 0-914868-24-1
        1. Dead Sea scrolls — Exhibitions. 2. Manuscripts, Hebrew — Jerusalem — Exhibi-
    tions. 3. Qumran site — Exhibitions. 4. Qumran community — Exhibitions. 5. Israel.
    Rashut ha-ʻatiqot — Library — Exhibitions. I. Sussmann, Ayala. II. Peled, Ruth.
    III. Israel. Rashut ha-ʻatiqot. IV. Library of Congress. V. New York Public Library.
    VI. M. H. de Young Memorial Museum. VII. Dead Sea scrolls. English & Hebrew.
    Selections. 1993.
    BM487.S37 1993   92-20476
    296.1ʹ55ʹ07473 — dc20   CIP

Printed in Singapore
10   9   8   7   6   5   4   3   2   1

Produced by
ARCHETYPE PRESS, INC., Washington, D.C.
Diane Maddex, Project Director
Robert L. Wiser, Art Director
Gretchen Smith Mui, Editorial Assistant

*Cover and opening pages: Detail from the Psalms Scroll (catalog no. 4; see pages 42–45). Copied ca.
30–50 C.E., this impressive scroll is a liturgical collection of psalms and hymns, comprising parts of
biblical as well as noncanonical psalms.*

CONTENTS

FOREWORD

John W. McCarter Jr.
President and CEO
The Field Museum

Just over a half century ago, in a remote cave by the Dead Sea at equal distance from the ancient cities of Jerusalem and Jericho, a young boy stumbled across a cluster of crumbling parchment scrolls, inadvertently making one of the greatest archaeological discoveries of the century. The Dead Sea Scrolls, as these extraordinary 2,000-year-old documents have come to be called, provide us with a window into the nature of Jewish religious and cultural activity during the period preceding the fall of the Second Temple.

The Field Museum is privileged to be able to present a selection of the Dead Sea Scrolls in Chicago. Amir Drori, director of the Israel Antiquities Authority, first proposed mounting a traveling exhibition of the Dead Sea Scrolls in the early 1990s. It is to his original vision that we owe thanks for facilitating this special presentation. His supportive staff includes Jacob Fisch, Hava Katz, Ruth Peled, Pnina Shor, and Ayala Sussmann. We are indebted to them all for their assistance. Our gratitude also goes out to Tzipora Rimon, Consul General of Israel, and her staff at the Consulate General of Israel in Chicago, and to the Israeli Ministry of Foreign Affairs Cultural Affairs Department.

We are supplementing the scrolls from Jerusalem with a number of other manuscripts from local collections. From our own holdings, we are presenting a rare illustrated volume by the first-century Jewish historian Josephus, published in English in 1778. From the Newberry Library in Chicago we are showing eight extraordinary objects, including the fourteenth-century Aramaic Targum Onqelos of the Pentateuch, the oldest complete Hebraica book in Chicago. We are grateful to Charles Cullen, president of the Newberry Library, and curators Paul Gehl and Paul Saenger, who helped us select the appropriate manuscripts for this exhibition. Susan Summerfield-Duke and Mary Wyly deserve our gratitude for their generous assistance.

We are also borrowing a complete modern Torah from the Spertus Museum of Chicago that demonstrates the continuity of the ancient scriptural tradition into the present. We value greatly our partnership with the Spertus, with which we will be collaborating in preparing both Jewish and interfaith programming for this exhibition. We thank Howard Sulkin, president, and curator Olga Weiss for their contributions, as well as Susan Bass Marcus, Glenn Ferdman, and Susan Webber, for their kind assistance.

The loans from these two institutions highlight the continued vitality of the Jewish textual legacy and situate the archaic scroll fragments from Israel within a broader context of Jewish religious practices throughout history. We are honored to display these treasures at the Field Museum, as they are some of the most significant Jewish artifacts in the city.

At the University of Chicago, our collaborators on the symposium series that accompanies the exhibition, we are grateful to Gene Gragg, director of the Oriental Institute. We are also thankful for the assistance provided by John Collins, professor in the Divinity School, and Norman Golb, professor of Jewish history and civilization.

The Field Museum has been generously aided in its programming and community outreach by the Dead Sea Scrolls exhibition community advisory panel, to which we are indebted. The community advisory panel is coordinated by the Museum's Center for Cultural Understanding and Change, led by Jacqueline Gray and Madeleine Tudor.

At the Field Museum, many members of the staff were involved. I wish to thank in particular Ariel Orlov, senior exhibit coordinator and exhibition developer for this exhibition; James L. Phillips, adjunct curator at the Museum and professor of archaeology at the University of Illinois at Chicago; Anne C. Haskel, director of sponsorships and international development; Catherine Sease, head of conservation; Sophia Shaw, director of exhibitions; Abigail Sinwell, manager of temporary exhibitions; and Ben Williams, librarian. I would also like to acknowledge the creativity and dedication of the exhibition and public programs team, led by Nel Fetherling, Matt Matcuk, Teresa Murray, Sue Stott, Dirk Urban, Thatcher Waller, and Dina Zissimopoulos.

PREFACE
TO THE
REVISED
EDITION

Amir Drori
Director
Israel Antiquities
Authority

It was with great pleasure that the Israel Antiquities Authority recently agreed to loan to the Field Museum a representative selection of original manuscripts of the Dead Sea Scrolls, together with related artifacts from the excavations at Qumran, where the scrolls were first uncovered in 1947. The story of the discovery of these fascinating two-thousand-year-old manuscripts has been told before, as has the tale of their purchase and the subsequent excavations in the caves of Qumran that revealed additional artifacts.

The difficulties in presenting the scrolls to the public, however, have frequently been distorted. It has always been our intent to unravel the meaning of these intriguing manuscripts and to present our findings to the public. Researchers have been toiling away at this task since the discovery of the scrolls. Hundreds of volumes of scholarship have been published, and many more are expected. Nevertheless, it may be years before the full implications of these texts are grasped in their entirety. As the keepers of these sacred and historical artifacts, our paramount concern has long been that the texts themselves be more widely viewed without endangering the state of their preservation.

It is toward this end that a carefully arranged showing of biblical and sectarian scrolls seemed a fitting endeavor. Although the scrolls were uncovered nearly half a century ago, they have not ceased to generate excitement and interest, either among scholars or with the general public. Much ink has been spilled on the mystery of these ancient texts, and today we are able to display a judiciously selected sampling that reveals the deeply rooted convictions of the communities they served. The addition to this exhibition of manuscripts reflecting on similarities and emphasizing, yet again, the common roots of the monotheistic religions well suits the beginning of a new millennium.

The Dead Sea Scrolls exhibition features fifteen fragmentary scrolls as well as a selection of archaeological artifacts excavated in Qumran and its environs in the Judean Desert. Written as far back as the third century B.C.E., but chiefly in the first century B.C.E. and first century C.E., the scrolls contain fragments of all the books of the Hebrew Bible (with the exception of Esther), as well as a complete text of Isaiah. Especially significant was the discovery of fragments of the Apocrypha, which previously had been known only in Greek and Latin. Now, for the first time, the scrolls give us Hebrew and Aramaic originals of central biblical passages we had been reading only in translation.

This exhibition was originally the product of fruitful collaboration among the Library of Congress in Washington, D.C., the New York Public Library, and the Israel Antiquities Authority. The accompanying catalog was first published in 1993 for venues at the Library of Congress, the New York Public Library, and the

M. H. de Young Memorial Museum in San Francisco. It has now been reprinted for the Field Museum in Chicago, where five additional scrolls are being presented for the first time. The catalog relates the story of the scrolls' discovery and illuminates their historical and archaeological context. We introduce the texts with transcriptions, translations, and explanations; explore the various theories concerning the nature of the Qumran community, its identity, and its theology; and discuss the challenges facing modern researchers as they struggle to reconstruct the texts and contexts from the thousands of fragments that remain. The exhibition enables visitors to understand the nature and working methods of archaeologists, historians, linguists, and paleographers.

Scores of talented individuals around the world have collaborated to make this complex undertaking possible. The initiative of Librarian of Congress James H. Billington, the late president of the New York Public Library, Father Timothy S. Healy, and the enthusiastic cooperation of their respective staffs facilitated the preparation of this project. At the Library of Congress, we owe thanks to Irene Chambers, Michael W. Grunberger, Doris A. Hamburg, and Tambra Johnson. We are grateful as well to Leonard S. Gold and Susan F. Saidenberg of the New York Public Library.

We also acknowledge the generosity of the funders of the 1993 exhibition: Shelby White, Leon Levy, Estanne Abraham-Fawer, Mr. and Mrs. Bernard Osher, the Wolfson Family Charitable Trust, and the assistance of the Israel Ministry of Foreign Affairs. Our warmest gratitude goes to the Project Judaica Foundation in Washington, D.C.; the foundation's support for this project has made possible both the exhibition and its catalog.

We wish to thank John W. McCarter Jr., president of the Field Museum; James L. Phillips, adjunct curator at the Museum; Ariel Orlov, senior exhibit coordinator and exhibition developer for this exhibition; Sophia Shaw, director of exhibitions; and Abigail Sinwell, manager of temporary exhibitions, all of whom have helped us develop and realize this expanded Dead Sea Scrolls exhibition at the Field Museum. Along with Teresa Murray, the exhibition designer, the above individuals have worked tirelessly toward our goal of presenting the Dead Sea Scrolls to the midwestern American public. We all believe that the success of the exhibition is due in large part to the efforts of these individuals.

The Dead Sea Scrolls sets these special manuscripts within what Father Healy aptly called a "living context." Such a setting is crucial for bringing these legendary artifacts back to the life they once had for those who wrote them and for showing their relevance for us two thousand years later.

THE DEAD SEA SCROLLS

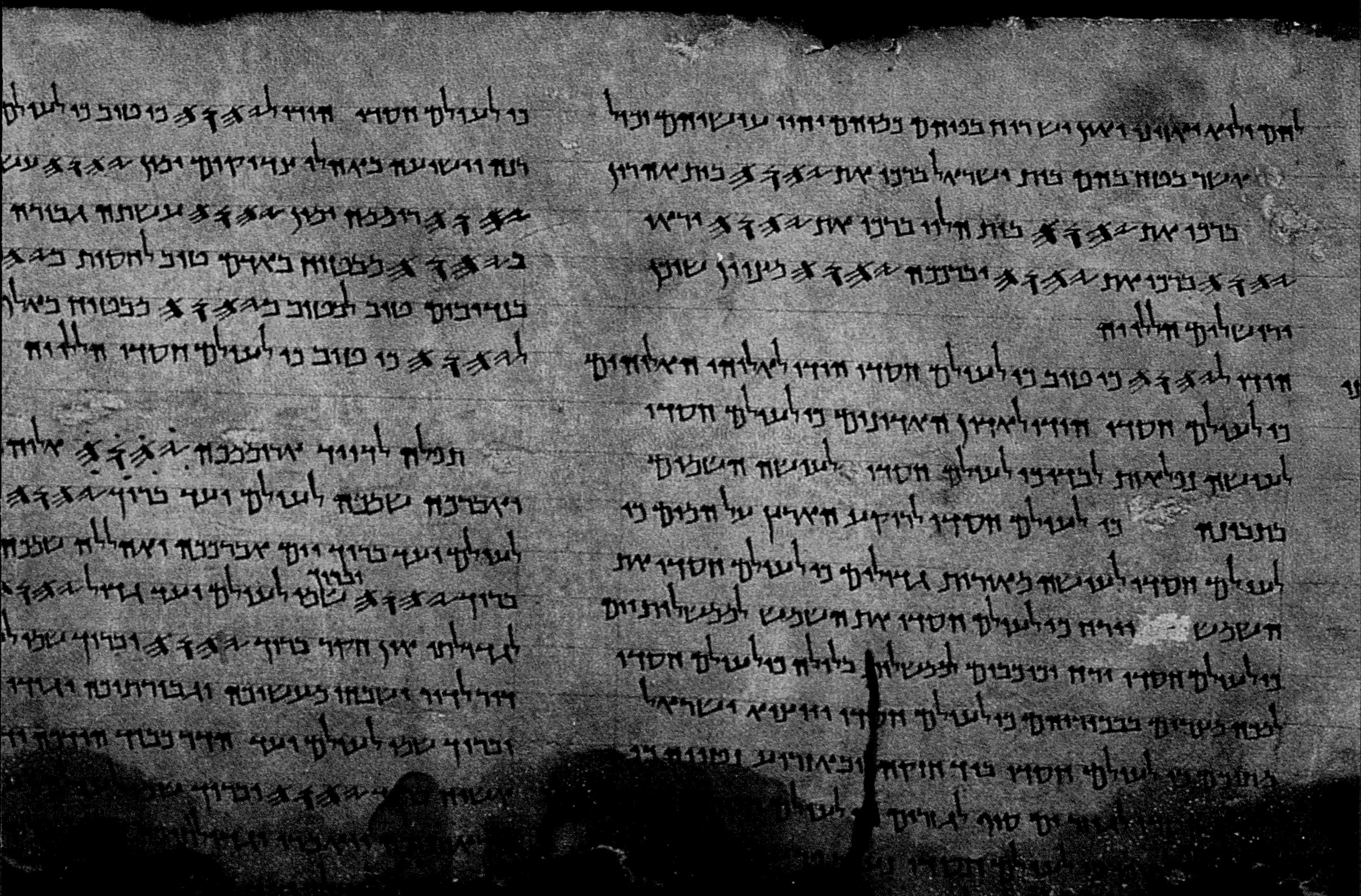

Introduction

Michael W. Grunberger

For the past several years the Dead Sea Scrolls have been the subject of intense public interest. Newspaper and television reports have chronicled—and fueled—the controversy surrounding the slow pace of scroll publication. The "liberation" of the scrolls occurred in late 1991, as unauthorized microfilms, photographic reproductions, and computer-driven reconstructions were made widely available.

The publication controversy is rooted in the special circumstances surrounding the acquisition of the scrolls. Within a decade of their discovery in 1947 all the scrolls but one (the Temple Scroll) had been uncovered and were housed in two Jerusalem repositories, one located in territory controlled by Israel and the other in territory controlled by Jordan. The scrolls in Israeli hands—larger and more intact—were published in short order.

When hostilities ceased in 1949 an intensive search for more scrolls was mounted. Eleven scroll caves were discovered. By far the most important was Cave 4, which contained thousands of fragments from hundreds of compositions. They were relocated to the Rockefeller Museum, where they were sorted and stored between glass plates. The myriad fragments were first arranged into compositions and then organized further according to scribal hand. This task fell to an eight-member team of scholars formed in 1953 as the official publication group, led by Père Roland de Vaux, head of the École Biblique in Jerusalem. No Jewish or Israeli scholars were invited to join the team.

The work proceeded slowly. The first volume of Discoveries in the Judaean Desert, the official publication series, was released in 1955. Volumes II and III appeared in 1961 and 1962 respectively. In 1965, with the publication of the Psalms Scroll (catalog no. 4) as Volume IV, the series title was changed to Discoveries in the Judaean Desert of Jordan, adding a dash of politics to the already volatile mix. The fifth volume, which was in press in 1967 and published in 1968, also carried this series title. In the wake of the 1967 Arab-Israeli War, the Rockefeller Museum building came under Israeli control, but the authorities chose to honor the original arrangements. The pace of publication slowed even further. Volume VI took a decade to complete, appearing only in 1977.

That year scholar Geza Vermes warned that "unless drastic measures are taken at once, the greatest and most valuable of all . . . Hebrew and Aramaic manuscript discoveries is likely to become the academic scandal par excellence of the twentieth century." His warning was not heeded: It took five years to publish Volume VII, and Volume VIII appeared eight years later, in 1990. Hershel Shanks, editor of *Biblical Archaeology Review,* took up the cause in the mid-1980s, using his popular magazine to attack restricted access to the manuscripts.

In 1988 Amir Drori was appointed head of the Israel Department of Antiquities (later Israel Antiquities Authority). Emanuel Tov, an Israeli scholar, was designated editor-in-chief of the scroll publication committee. Under the latter's direction, deadlines were set and the number of scholars with scroll assignments grew from eight to more than fifty.

Despite these steps public pressure increased as Hershel Shanks and others recast the issue as one of intellectual freedom and the right of all scholars—not just members of the scroll "cartel"—to have access to the scrolls. Editorials supporting his position appeared in newspapers across America. Some persons even asserted that access was restricted because the scrolls contained untold secrets that, once revealed, would undermine the foundations of established religions. The Israel Antiquities Authority believed that the steps already taken would lay to rest the issue by the year 2000.

As often happens, however, events overtook debate. In the fall of 1991 the Huntington Library announced that it would make available to scholars security copies of photographs of the scrolls deposited in its vaults. Next, two Hebrew Union College scholars developed a computer program that reconstructed Cave 4 texts from a decades-old concordance. The first fascicle of the reconstructions was published in late 1991, as was a two-volume edition of scroll photographs. Both the computer reconstruction and the facsimile edition were issued by the Biblical Archaeology Society, headed by Hershel Shanks. Closing the circle, the Israel Antiquities Authority announced that it would be issuing an authorized microfiche edition, complete with detailed indexes.

EXHIBITIONS OF THE DEAD SEA SCROLLS

The first exhibition of the Dead Sea Scrolls in the United States was held at the Library of Congress in 1949. Three scrolls—the Isaiah Scroll, the Habakkuk Commentary, and the Community Rule—were displayed. From the Library the exhibition traveled to Baltimore, Durham, North Carolina, Chicago (at the Oriental Institute), and Worcester, Massachusetts.

In 1965 the Smithsonian Institution, in cooperation with the government of Jordan and the Palestine Archaeological Museum (the Rockefeller Museum), Jerusalem, mounted an international traveling exhibition entitled *Scrolls from the Wilderness of the Dead Sea.* This exhibiton presented a full range of fragmentary scrolls (including catalog no. 4), as well as related artifacts. From Washington, D.C., it traveled to Philadelphia, Berkeley and Claremont in California, Omaha, and Baltimore, then to Ottawa and Toronto, and finally to England.

The exhibition *Treasures of the Holy Land,* shown at the Metropolitan Museum of Art in New York in 1986–87, and traveling on to Los Angeles and Houston, included one scroll, the Habakkuk Commentary, from the Shrine of the Book in Jerusalem. The New York Public Libraary included the Nahum Commentary, also from the Shrine of the Book, in its 1988 exhibition *A Sign and a Witness: 2000 Years of Hebrew Books and Illuminated Manuscripts.*

The present Field Museum exhibition originated at the Library of Congress in 1993 and subsequently traveled to the New York Public Library and the M. H. de Young Memorial Museum in San Francisco. In 1994 the tour of the scrolls was extended to the Biblioteca Apostolica Vaticana in Rome, moving the following year to the Israel Museum in Jerusalem. The exhibition again toured in 1998–99 to the Kelvingrove Art Gallery and Museum in Glasgow, Scotland; the Romish-Germanisches Museum in Cologne, Germany and the Stiftsbibliothek in St. Gallen, Switzerland.

This exhibition catalog is divided into two main sections. The first, "From the Scroll Caves," describes the fifteen scroll fragments included in the exhibition. The curatorial descriptions of the scrolls include the following elements:

1. An exhibit number.

2. A translated name for the scroll (e.g., Hosea Commentary).

3. A transliterated name (e.g., Pesher Hoshe'a).

4. The name of the scroll in Hebrew.

5. The scroll's classification number. The traditional notation generally includes some or all of the following information: the number of the cave in which the fragment was uncovered, the location of the cave, the number assigned to the overall fragment, an abbreviated name, and the specific fragment number (e.g., the classification number 4QpHos^a would indicate Cave 4, Qumran, Pesher Hoshe'a, Fragment a).

6. An approximation of the period in which the scroll was copied.

7. Measurements of the fragment in centimeters and inches.

8. A description of the scroll. References to scholarly articles and monographs on the fragment are located at the foot of the entry.

9. A translation of the scroll by a leading scholar as well as a transcription into Hebrew script of a portion of the text. Translated and transcribed text enclosed in brackets indicates letters, words, or passages supplied by the translator or transcriber. Large brackets around the scroll fragments assist the reader in locating the transcribed portions.

The second section, "From the Qumran Ruin," presents artifacts excavated at the nearby Qumran ruin in addition to a number of items from the caves. They are organized by material, such as pottery, wood, leather, and textiles. Brief introductions and captions describe the materials and their uses.

It is our hope that this exhibition and catalog will lead to a greater understanding of the turbulent period in which the Dead Sea Scrolls were written and copied—a period that set the stage for the emergence of modern Judaism and Christianity. We also hope to encourage a better understanding of the challenges and complexities connected with scroll research, aiming to create a realistic expectation of its potential fruits as well as an appreciation for the considerable patience, skill, and persistence of those charged with gathering the harvest.

Abbreviations

B.C.E.   Before the Common Era, an alternate designation for B.C.

C.E.   Common Era, an alternate designation for A.D.

ca.   *Circa,* about or around a date

vac   Space left intentionally by the scribe

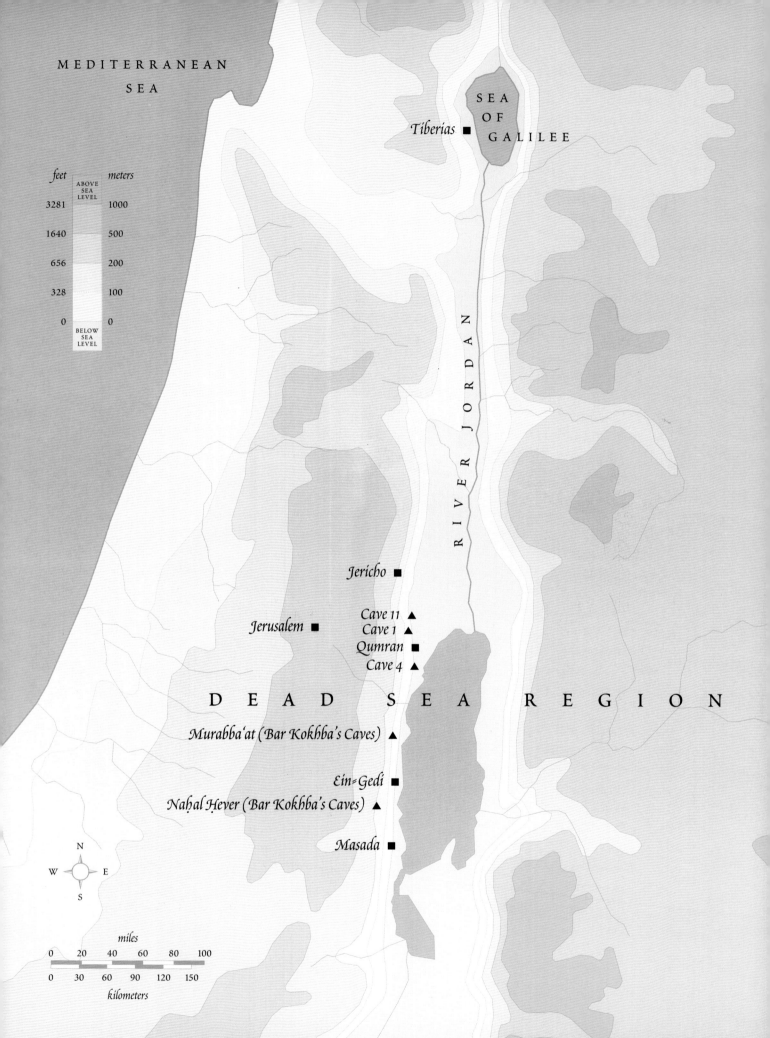

MEDITERRANEAN
SEA

feet   meters

ABOVE
SEA
LEVEL

3281   1000

1640   500

656   200

328   100

0   0

BELOW
SEA
LEVEL

SEA
OF
GALILEE

Tiberias ■

RIVER JORDAN

Jericho ■

Cave 11 ▲
Cave 1 ▲
Jerusalem ■   Qumran ■
Cave 4 ▲

D E A D   S E A   R E G I O N

Murabba'at (Bar Kokhba's Caves) ▲

Ein-Gedi ■

Naḥal Ḥever (Bar Kokhba's Caves) ▲

Masada ■

N
W — E
S

miles
0   20   40   60   80   100

0   30   60   90   120   150
kilometers

Ancient Hebrew scrolls accidentally discovered in 1947 by a Bedouin boy have kindled popular enthusiasm as well as serious scholarly interest over the past half century. The source of this excitement is what these Dead Sea Scrolls reveal about the history of the Second Temple period (520 B.C.E.–70 C.E.), particularly from the second century B.C.E. until the destruction of the Second Temple in 70 C.E. — a time of crucial developments in the crystallization of the monotheistic religions.

The Judean Desert, a region reputedly barren, has defied preconceptions and yielded an unprecedented treasure. The young Ta'amireh shepherd was certainly unaware of destiny when his innocent search for a stray goat led to the fateful discovery of Hebrew scrolls in a long-untouched cave. One discovery led to another, and eleven scroll-yielding caves and a habitation site eventually were uncovered. Since 1947 the site of these discoveries — the Qumran region (the desert plain and the adjoining mountainous ridge) and the Qumran site — have been subjected to countless probes; not a stone has remained unturned in the desert, not an aperture unprobed. The Qumran settlement has been exhaustively excavated.

The first trove found by the Bedouin in the Judean Desert consisted of seven large scrolls from Cave 1. Shortly before the establishment of the state of Israel, Professor E. L. Sukenik of the Hebrew University acquired three of the scrolls from a Christian Arab antiquities dealer in Bethlehem. The remaining four scrolls reached the hands of Mar Athanasius Yeshua Samuel, Metropolitan of the Syrian Jacobite Monastery of St. Mark in Jerusalem. In 1949 he traveled to the United States with the scrolls, but five years went by before the prelate found a purchaser.

On June 1, 1954, Mar Samuel placed an advertisement in the *Wall Street Journal* offering "The Four Dead Sea Scrolls" for sale. The advertisement was brought to the attention of Yigael Yadin, Professor Sukenik's son, who had just retired as chief of staff of the Israel Defense Forces and had reverted to his primary vocation, archaeology. With the aid of intermediaries, the four scrolls were purchased from Mar Samuel for $250,000. Thus, the scrolls that had eluded Yadin's father because of the war were now at his disposal. Part of the purchase price was contributed by D. S. Gottesman, a New York philanthropist. His heirs sponsored construction of the Shrine of the Book in Jerusalem's Israel Museum, in which these unique manuscripts are exhibited to the public.

The seven scrolls from Cave 1, now housed together in the Shrine of the Book, are Isaiah A, Isaiah B, the Habakkuk Commentary, the Thanksgiving Scroll, the Community Rule (or the Manual of Discipline), the War Rule (or the War of Sons of Light Against the Sons of Darkness), and the Genesis Apocryphon, the last being in Aramaic. All the large scrolls have been published.

TREASURES FROM THE JUDEAN DESERT

Ayala Sussmann and Ruth Peled

The Caves. At least a year elapsed between the discovery of the scrolls in 1947 and the initiation of a systematic archaeological investigation of the Qumran region. The northern Dead Sea area, the location of Qumran, became and remained part of Jordan until 1967. The search for scroll material rested in the hands of the Bedouin, who continued to explore the Cave 1 site.

Early in 1949 the cave site was finally identified by the archaeological authorities of Jordan. G. Lankester Harding, director of the Jordanian Antiquities Department, undertook to excavate Cave 1 with Père Roland de Vaux, a French Dominican priest who headed the École Biblique in Jerusalem. Exploration of the cave, which lay one kilometer north of Wadi Qumran, yielded at least seventy fragments, including bits of the original seven scrolls. This discovery established the provenance of the purchased scrolls. Also recovered were archaeological artifacts that confirmed the scroll dates suggested by paleographic study.

The Bedouin continued to search for scrolls, as these scraps of leather were a source of income. Because Cave 1 had been exhausted by archaeological excavation, the fresh material that the Bedouin were offering proved that Cave 1 was not an isolated phenomenon in the desert and that other caves with manuscripts also existed.

The years between 1951 and 1956 were marked by accelerated activity in both the search for caves and the archaeological excavation of sites related to the manuscripts. An eight-kilometer-long strip of cliffs was thoroughly investigated. Of the eleven caves that yielded manuscripts, five were discovered by the Bedouin and six by archaeologists. Some of the caves were particularly rich in material. Cave 3 preserved two oxidized rolls of beaten copper (the Copper Scroll), containing a lengthy roster of real or imaginary hidden treasures—a tantalizing enigma to this day. Cave 4 was particularly rich in material: 15,000 fragments from at least six hundred composite texts were found there. The last manuscript cave discovered, Cave 11, was located in 1956, providing extensive documents, including the Psalms Scroll (catalog no. 4), an Aramaic *targum* (translation) of Job, and the Temple Scroll, the longest (about twenty-nine feet) of the Qumran manuscripts. The Temple Scroll was acquired by Yigael Yadin in 1967 and is now housed alongside the first seven scrolls in the Shrine of the Book at the Israel Museum in Jerusalem. All the remaining manuscripts, sizable texts as well as minute fragments, are stored in the Rockefeller Museum building in Jerusalem, the premises of the Israel Antiquities Authority.

Khirbet Qumran (The Qumran Ruin). Père de Vaux gradually realized the need to identify a habitation site close to the caves. Excavating such a site, he thought, could provide clues that would help identify the people who deposited the scrolls.

The ruins of Qumran lie on a barren terrace between the limestone cliffs of the Judean Desert and a fossil lake bed along the Dead Sea. The excavations

Mar Samuel's 1954 advertisement in the Wall Street Journal *attracted attention and eventually a buyer.*

Plates, bowls, and goblets were found in one room at Qumran, with dozens of vessels piled one on top of the other. This room probably served as a pantry near the assembly room, which may have been a dining room.

uncovered a complex of structures, 262 by 328 feet (80 by 100 meters), preserved to a considerable height. According to de Vaux, the structures were neither military nor private but rather communal in character.

Nearby were remains of burials. Pottery uncovered was identical with that of Cave 1 and confirmed the link with the nearby caves. Following the initial excavations, de Vaux suggested that this site was the wilderness retreat established by the Essene sect, which was alluded to by ancient historians. The sectarians inhabited neighboring locations, most likely caves, tents, and solid structures, but depended on the center for communal facilities such as stores of food and water. Excavations conducted in 1956 and 1958 at the neighboring site of 'En Feshkha proved it to be the agricultural adjunct of Qumran.

The final report on the Qumran settlement excavations is pending, but the results are known through preliminary publications.

The discovery of the Dead Sea Scrolls caused heated controversy in scholarly circles over their date and the identity of the community they represented.

DATING OF THE SCROLLS

Professor Sukenik, after initially defining the time span of the scrolls as the Second Temple period, recognized their special significance and advocated the theory that they were remnants of the library of the Essenes. At the time, however, he was vociferously opposed by a number of scholars who doubted the antiquity as well as the authenticity of the texts. Lingering in the memory of learned circles was the notorious Shapira affair of 1883. M. Shapira, a Jerusalem antiquities dealer, announced the discovery of an ancient text of Deuteronomy. His texts, allegedly inscribed on fifteen leather strips, caused a huge stir in Europe and were even exhibited at the British Museum. Shortly thereafter, the leading European scholars of the day denounced the writings as rank forgeries.

Today scholarly opinion regarding the time span and background of the Dead Sea Scrolls is anchored in historical, paleographic, and linguistic evidence, corroborated firmly by carbon 14 datings. Some manuscripts were written and copied in the third century B.C.E., but the bulk of the material, particularly the texts that reflect on a sectarian community, are originals or copies from the first century B.C.E.; a number of texts date from as late as the years preceding the destruction of the site in 68 C.E. at the hands of the Roman legions.

THE ESSENES

The Qumran sect's origins are postulated by some scholars to be in the communities of the *Ḥasidim,* the pious anti-Hellenistic circles that were formed in the early days of the Maccabees. The *Ḥasidim* may have been the precursors of the Essenes, who were concerned about growing Hellenization and strove to abide by the Torah.

Archaeological and historical evidence indicates that Qumran was founded in the second half of the second century B.C.E., during the time of the Maccabean dynasty. A hiatus in the occupation of the site is linked to evidence of a huge earthquake. Qumran was abandoned about the time of the Roman incursion of 68 C.E., two years before the collapse of Jewish self-government in Judea and the destruction of the Temple in Jerusalem in 70 C.E.

The chief sources of information for the history of this fateful time span are the Qumran scrolls and the excavations, but earlier information on the Essenes was provided by their contemporaries: Josephus Flavius, Philo of Alexandria, and Pliny the Elder.

The historian Josephus relates the division of the Jews of the Second Temple period into three orders: the Sadducees, the Pharisees, and the Essenes. The Sadducees included mainly the priestly and aristocratic families; the Pharisees constituted the lay circles; and the Essenes were a separatist group, part of which formed an ascetic monastic community that retreated to the wilderness. The exact political and religious affinities of each of these groups, as well as their development and interrelationships, are still relatively obscure and are the source of widely disparate scholarly views.

The crisis that brought about the secession of the Essenes from mainstream Judaism is thought to have occurred when the Maccabean ruling princes Jonathan (160–142 B.C.E.) and Simeon (142–134 B.C.E.) usurped the office of high priest (which included secular duties), much to the consternation of conservative Jews; some of them could not tolerate the situation and denounced the new rulers. The persecution of the Essenes and their leader, the "teacher of righteousness," probably elicited the sect's apocalyptic visions. These included the overthrow of "the wicked priest" of Jerusalem and of the evil people and, in the dawn of the Messianic Age, the recognition of their community as the true Israel. The retreat of these Jews into the desert would enable them "to separate themselves from the congregation of perverse men" (1Q Serekh 5:2).

A significant feature of the Essene sect is its calendar, which was based on a solar system of 364 days, unlike the common Jewish calendar, which was lunar and consisted of 354 days. It is not clear how the sectarian calendar was reconciled, as was the normative Jewish calendar, with the astronomical time system (see catalog no. 8). The sectarian calendar was always reckoned from a Wednesday, the day on which God created the luminaries. The year consisted of fifty-two weeks, divided into four seasons of thirteen weeks each, and the festivals consistently fell on the same days of the week. A similar solar system was long familiar from pseudepigraphic works. The sectarian calendar played a weighty role in the schism of the community from the rest of Judaism, as the festivals and fast days of the sect were ordinary work days for the mainstream community and vice versa. The author of the Book of Jubilees accuses the followers of the lunar calendar of turning secular "days of impurity" into "festivals and holy days" (Jubilees 6:36–37).

The sectarians persisted in a separatist existence through two centuries, occupying themselves with study and a communal way of life that included worship, prayer, and work. It is clear, however, that large groups of adherents also lived in towns and villages outside the Qumran area.

The word *Essene* is never distinctly mentioned in the scrolls. How then can we attribute either the writings or the sites of the Judean Desert to the Essenes?

The argument in favor of this ascription can be supported by the tripartite division of Judaism referred to in Qumran writings (for example, in the Nahum Commentary) into Ephraim, Menasseh, and Judah, corresponding to the Pharisees, the Sadducees, and the Essenes. As the Essenes refer to themselves in the scrolls as Judah, it is quite clear whom they regarded themselves to be. Moreover, their religious concepts and beliefs as attested in the scrolls conform to those recorded by contemporary writers and stand in sharp contrast to those of the other known Jewish groups.

In most cases the principles of the Essene way of life and beliefs are described by contemporaneous writers in language similar to the self-descriptions found in the scrolls. Customs described in ancient sources as Essene—such as the probationary period for new members, the strict hierarchy practiced in the organization of the sect, their frequent ablutions, and communal meals—are all echoed in the scrolls. From the Community Rule: "Communally they shall eat and communally they shall bless and communally they shall take counsel" (1Q Serekh 6:1). Finally, the location of the sect is assigned to the Dead Sea area by the Roman historian Pliny the Elder.

Although this evidence is accepted by the majority of scholars in identifying the Essenes with the Qumran settlement and the manuscripts found in the surrounding caves, a number of scholars remain vehemently opposed. Some propose that the site was a military garrison or even a winter villa. The scrolls are viewed as an eclectic collection, neither necessarily inscribed in the Dead

Talmudist and educator Solomon Schechter examines fragments of Hebrew manuscripts in 1896 from the famous Cairo Genizah, or store-room for discarded Hebrew writings that he rediscovered in the attic of the ninth-century Ben Ezra Synagogue.

Sea area nor sectarian in nature. Perhaps they are even the remains of the library of the Temple in Jerusalem, hidden during the Jewish revolt. Other scholars view the texts as the writings of forerunners or even followers of Jesus—Jewish Christians—who still observed Jewish law.

The Qumran Library

The writings recovered in the Qumran environs has restored to us a voluminous corpus of Jewish documents dating from the third century B.C.E. to 68 C.E., demonstrating the rich literary activity of Second Temple–period Jewry. The collection comprises varied documents, most of them of a distinct religious bent. The chief categories represented are biblical, apocryphal or pseudepigraphical, and sectarian writings. The study of this original library has demonstrated that the boundaries between these categories are far from clear-cut.

The biblical manuscripts include what are probably the earliest copies of these texts to have come down to us. Most of the books of the Bible are represented in the collection. Some books exist in a large number of copies; others are represented on mere scraps of parchment. The biblical texts display considerable similarity to the standard Masoretic (received) text. This, however, is not always the rule, and many texts diverge from the Masoretic. For example, some of the texts of Samuel from Cave 4 follow the Septuagint, the Greek version of the Bible translated in the third to second centuries B.C.E. Indeed, Qumran has yielded copies of the Septuagint in Greek.

The biblical scrolls in general have provided many new readings that facilitate the reconstruction of the textual history of the Old Testament. It is also significant that several manuscripts of the Bible, including the Leviticus Scroll (catalog no. 3), are inscribed not in the Jewish script dominant at the time but rather in the ancient paleo-Hebrew script.

A considerable number of apocryphal and pseudepigraphic texts are preserved at Qumran, where original Hebrew and Aramaic versions of these Jewish compositions of the Second Temple period were first encountered. These writings, which are not included in the canonical Jewish scriptures, were preserved by different Christian churches and were transmitted in Greek, Ethiopic, Syriac, Armenian, and other translations.

Some of these are narrative texts closely related to biblical compositions, such as the Book of Jubilees and Enoch (catalog no. 9), whereas others are independent works—for example, Tobit and Ben Sira. Apparently some of these compositions were treated by the Qumran community as canonical and were studied by them.

The most original and unique group of writings from Qumran are the sectarian ones, which were practically unknown until their discovery in 1947. An exception is the Damascus Document (or Damascus Covenant), which lacked a definite identification before the discoveries of the Dead Sea area (see catalog no. 1). This widely varied literature reveals the beliefs and customs of a pietistic commune, probably centered at Qumran, and includes rules and ordinances, biblical commentaries, apocalyptic visions, and liturgical works, generally attributed to the last quarter of the second century B.C.E. and onward.

The "rules," the collections of rules and instructions reflecting the practices of the commune, are exemplified by the Damascus Document (catalog no. 1), the Community Rule (catalog no. 6), and Some Torah Precepts (catalog no. 7). Here we witness a considerable corpus of legal material *(Halakhah)* that has much in common with the rabbinic tradition preserved at a later date in the Mishnah (the compendium of mostly legal regulations and beliefs fundamental to rabbinic Judaism after the second century C.E). The *Halakhah* emerging from the sectarian writings seems to be corroborated by the sectarian *Halakhah* referred to in rabbinic sources.

The biblical commentaries *(pesharim)*, such as the Habakkuk Commentary, the Nahum Commentary, and the Hosea Commentary (catalog no. 5), are attested solely at Qumran and grew out of the sect's eschatological presuppositions. The Scriptures were scanned by the sect for allusions to current and future events. These allusions could be understood only by the sectarians themselves, because only they possessed "eyes to see"—their distinct eschatological vision. Liturgical works figure prominently among the sectarian manuscripts at Qumran because of the centrality of prayer in this period. The Thanksgiving Psalms *(Hodayot)* are of two types: those characterized by a personal tone, attributed by some to the "teacher of righteousness," and the communal type, referring to a group.

Many more compositions deserve mention, but this brief survey demonstrates the major role played by the Dead Sea Scrolls in improving our comprehension of this pivotal moment in Jewish history.

← *ca. 6th century* B.C.E. *Canonization of the Torah (Pentateuch), the first of the three major divisions of the Hebrew Bible*

← *ca. 4th century* B.C.E. *Canonization of the Nevi'im (Prophets), the second of the three major divisions of the Hebrew Bible*

← *ca. mid-3rd century* B.C.E. *Completion of the Septuagint (translation of the Pentateuch into Greek)*

ca. 200 B.C.E.–*100* C.E. *Apocryphal and Apocalyptic literature*

KEY FIGURES

POLITICAL AND MILITARY EVENTS

← *586* B.C.E. *Babylonians destroy Jerusalem; beginning of Babylonian exile*

← *538* B.C.E. *Cyrus, ruler of Persia, permits exiles to return to Judea*

← *333* B.C.E. *Alexander the Great extends Greek rule to Palestine and Egypt*

← *323* B.C.E. *Alexander's empire divided into three parts: Antigonids in Macedonia, Seleucids in Syria, and Ptolemies in Egypt*

← *301* B.C.E. *Ptolemies' rule over Judea begins*

← *198* B.C.E. *Seleucids' rule over Judea begins*

← *168* B.C.E. *Hasmonean revolt*

← *164* B.C.E. *Temple purified by Judas Maccabeus*

■ *63* B.C.E. *Rome occupies Jerusalem*

THE HASMONEAN DYNASTY

Aristobulus 104–103 B.C.E.

Alexander Jannaeus 103–76 B.C.E.

Judas Maccabeus 166–160 B.C.E.

Salome Alexandra 76–67 B.C.

Jonathan 160–142 B.C.E.

Aristobulus II 67–63 B.C.

Simeon 142–134 B.C.E.

Hyrcanus II 63–40 B.C.E.

John Hyrcanus 134–104 B.C.E.

Antigonus II 40–37 B.C.E.

BEFORE THE COMMON ERA

160   150   140   130   120   110   100   90   80   70   60   50   4

ca. 40–50 C.E. Beginnings of the New Testament

ca. 90 C.E. Canonization of the Ketuvim (Hagiographa), the third of the three major divisions of the Hebrew Bible →

ca. 200 C.E. Mishnah edited by Rabbi Judah the Prince →

Hillel ca. 80 B.C.E.–ca. 9 C.E.

Philo of Alexandria ca. 30 B.C.E.–45 C.E.

Jesus of Nazareth ca. 4 B.C.E.–29 C.E.

Pontius Pilate procurator of Judea 26–36 C.E.

Josephus Flavius ca. 38–100 C.E.

37 B.C.E. Herod conquers Jerusalem

5–41 C.E. Judea, Samaria, and
umea placed under procurators

44–66 C.E. Rule of the procurators

66 C.E. Revolt against Rome

ca. 68 C.E. Roman legions destroy the Qumran settlement

70 C.E. Roman legions conquer Jerusalem

73 C.E. Masada falls to Rome

THE HERODIAN DYNASTY

Herod the Great 37–4 B.C.E.

Archelaus 4 B.C.E.–6 C.E.

Herod Antipas 4 B.C.E.–39 C.E.

Herod Philip 4 B.C.E.–34 C.E.

Agrippa I 41–44 C.E.

Agrippa II 50–ca. 92 C.E.

THE COMMON ERA

| 30 | 20 | 10 | ◆ | 10 | 20 | 30 | 40 | 50 | 60 | 70 | 80 | 90 |

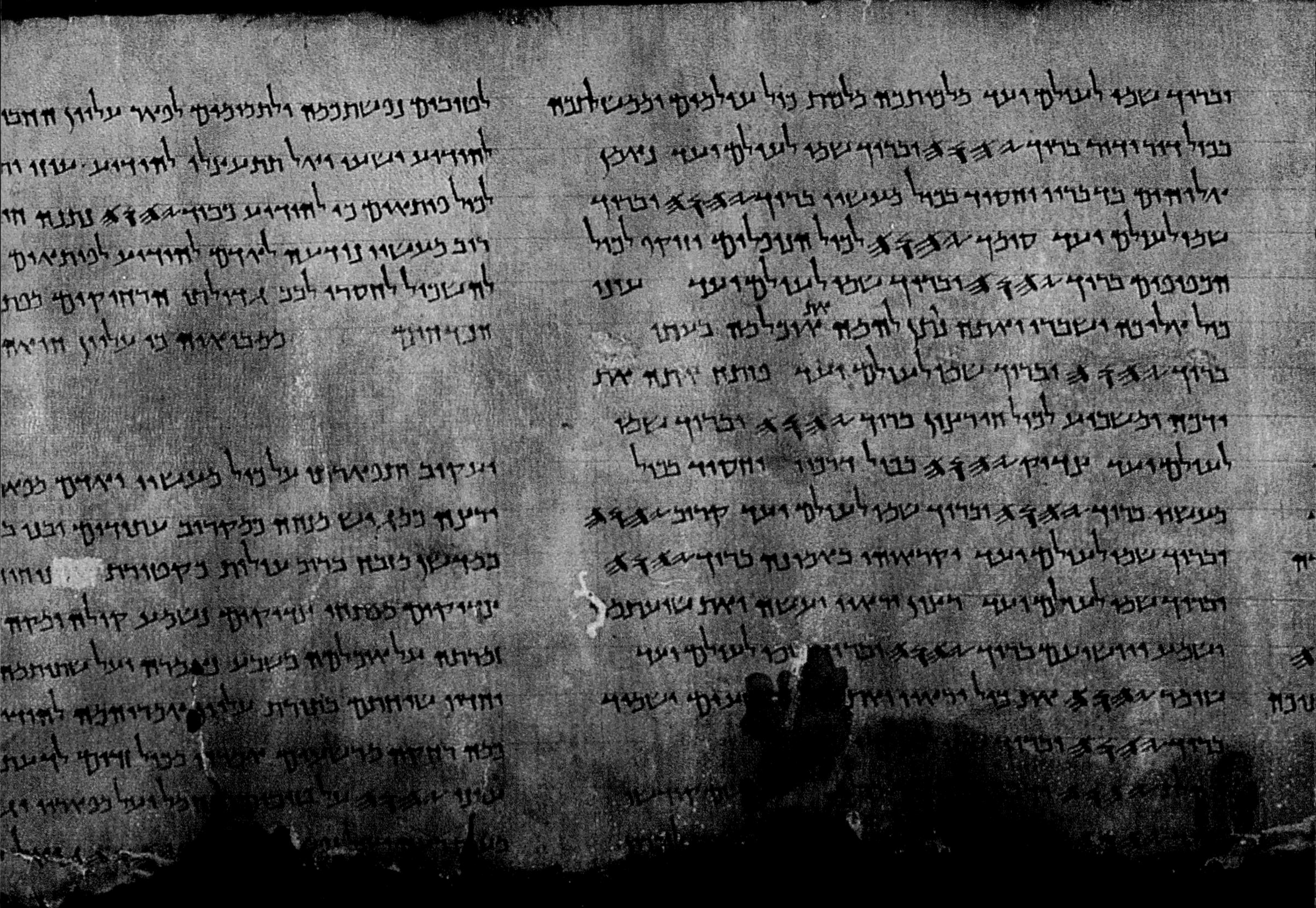

CATALOG

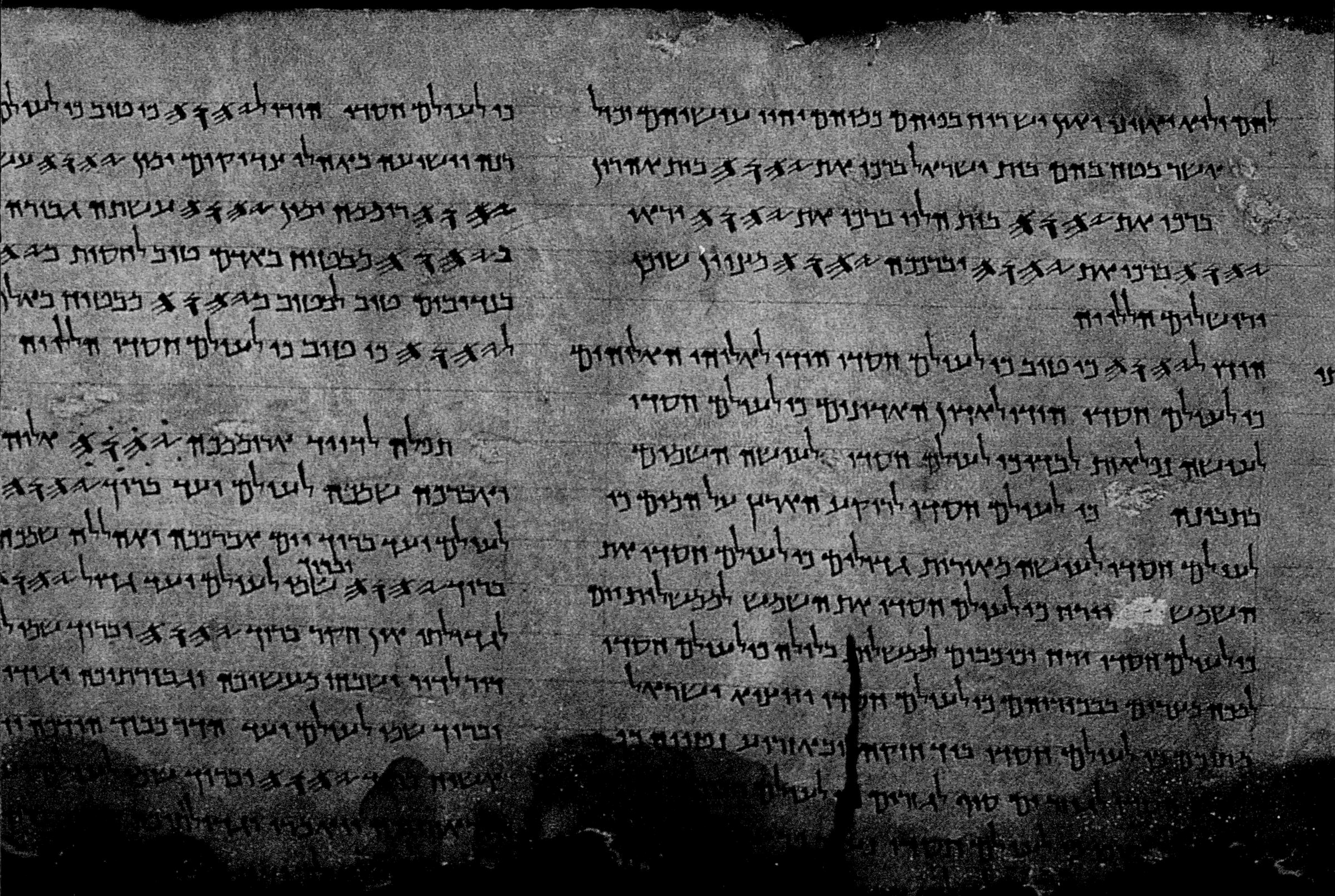

FROM THE
SCROLL CAVES

I

DAMASCUS
DOCUMENT
BRIT DAMESEK
ברית דמשק
4Q271(D^f)
Copied late first
century B.C.E.
10.9 × 9.3 cm
(4¼ × 3⅝ in.)

Solomon Schechter's discovery of the Damascus Document (or Damascus Covenant) in the Cairo Genizah a century ago (see page 22) may be regarded as the true starting point of modern scroll research. In his *Fragments of a Zadokite Work,* published in 1910, he presented two copies of a medieval text that he identified as being of a sectarian nature. Almost a half century passed before inscribed scrolls discovered in the Judean Desert confirmed the Second Temple–period dating that Schechter assigned the text in 1910.

Scholarly controversy has long marked the study of this document, which dates to the late Herodian period (37–4 B.C.E.). Not long after its publication, some scholars began to call it the Damascus Document because it refers to a covenant made in "Damascus." However, the meaning of this name, whether geographical or symbolic (see Amos 5:26), is still debated. As many as seventeen suggestions have been offered as to the identification of the community represented in the Damascus Document, including Zadokites (descendants of the ancient high priest Zadok), Pharisees, Essenes, and early Christians. Only the discovery of similar material in the caves associated with the Qumran site confirmed a link between the Damascus Document and the literature of the Qumran community.

The Damascus Document includes two elements. The first is an admonition that implores the congregation to remain faithful to the covenant of those who retreated from Judea to the "Land of Damascus." The second lists statutes dealing with vows and oaths, the tribunal, witnesses and judges, purification of water, Sabbath laws, and ritual cleanliness.

The order of the ancient Qumran text differs from that of the medieval text found in the Genizah, which also lacks the beginning, the end, and some of the statutes that we are now familiar with through the Qumran text.

One of the eight fragments of the Damascus Document uncovered in Cave 4, the passage displayed here extends the biblical injunction concerning integrity in buying and selling (Lev. 25:14) to the requirement of full disclosure in arranging marriages. Essene men who married took every precaution to ascertain the good moral and physical characters of their wives, as indicated by Josephus (*The Jewish War,* II, 161). This text is not familiar from the Genizah manuscripts and is therefore of great significance.

The right-hand margin is incomplete. The left-hand margin was sewn to another piece of parchment, as evidenced by the remaining stitches.

References

Baumgarten, J. M. *Qumran Cave 4: XIII. The Damascus Document (4Q266–273).* Discoveries in the Judaean Desert, XVIII. Oxford, 1996.

Rabin, C. *The Zadokite Documents.* Oxford, 1958.

Schechter, S. *Fragments of a Zadokite Work: Documents of Jewish Sectaries.* Cambridge, England, 1910.

1.   . . . with money . . .

2.   . . . [his means did not] suffice to [return it to him] and the year [for redemption appproaches?] . . .

3.   . . . and may God release him? from his sins. Let not [   ] in one, for

4.   it is an abomination. . . . And concerning what he said *(Lev. 25:14)*, ["When you sell

5.   anything to or buy anything from] your neighbor, you shall not defraud one another," this is the expli[cation . . .

6.   . . .] everything that he knows that is found . . .

7.   . . . and he knows that he is wronging him, whether it concerns man or beast. And if

8.   [a man gives his daughter to another ma]n, let him disclose all her blemishes to him, lest he bring upon himself the judgement

9.   [of the curse which is said *(Deut. 27:18)*] (of the one) that "makes the blind to wander out of the way." Moreover, he should not give her to one unfit for her, for

10. [that is Kila'yim, (plowing with) o]x and ass and wearing wool and linen together. Let no man bring

11. [a woman into the holy [   ] who has had sexual experience, whether she had such experience

12. [in the home] of her father or as a widow who had intercourse after she was widowed. And any woman

13. [upon whom] there is a bad name in her maidenhood in her father's home, let no man take her, except

14. [upon examination] by reliable [women] who have clear knowledge, by command of the Supervisor over

15. [the Many. After]ward he may take her, and when he takes her he shall act in accordance with the law . . . and he shall not tell . . .

16. [   ]L[   ]

Transcription and translation by J. M. Baumgarten

1. [ ] בכסף [ ]

2. [ ] [שנת ה] [והגי] [שיב לה]דיו ה[שיגה לוא וידו]

3. [ ] אל [עוונותיו] [ל]יעזוב ואל[ ]

4. [ ] [תמכור] כי אמר ואשר היא תועבה כי [באחת]

5. [פרו]ש וזה עמיתו את איש תונו לוא עמיתך [מיד קנה או ממכר]

6. [ ] תן [ ] ... ימצא אשר יודע הוא אשר בכול [ ]

7. ואם ובהמה באדם בו מועל הוא אשר יודע והוא [ ]

8. למה לו יספר מומיה כול את לאי]ש איש יתן [בת

יביא עליו את משפט

9. להכי יתנהה אל וגם בדרך עור משגה אמ]ר אשר [הארור

לאשר לוא הוכן

10. איש יבא אל יחדיו ופשתים{ צמר ולבוש וחמור ש]ור כלאים ו[הוא .10

11. ידעה ואשר מדבר{ מעשה לעשות ידעה אשר הקו]דש ב[ם] [אשה .11

12. וכול התארמלה מאשר נשכבה אשר אלמנה או אביה ב]בית מעשה

13. אם כי איש יקחה אל אביה בבית בבתוליה רע ש]ם עליה [אשר .13

14. על אשר המבקר ממאמר ברורות וידעות נאמנות [נשים בראות .14

15. ע י]גיד [ולוא כמ]פט יעשה אותה ובלוקחו יקחנה ואח]ר [הרבים .15

16. [ל] [ל] [ ] .16

The King Jonathan mentioned in this text can be no other than the Hasmonean monarch Alexander Jannaeus (103–76 B.C.E.). His coins, although inscribed in Greek with "King Alexander," have "King Jonathan" in Hebrew.

The discovery of a prayer for the welfare of a Hasmonean king among the Qumran texts is unexpected because the sectarians vehemently opposed the Hasmoneans; they may even have settled in the remote desert to avoid contact with the Hasmonean authorities and priesthood. If this is indeed a composition that clashes with Qumran views, it is a single occurrence among six hundred nonbiblical manuscripts. However, there is a high possibility, perhaps also alluded to in the Nahum Commentary, that Jonathan-Jannaeus, unlike the other Hasmonean rulers, was favored by the Dead Sea sect, at least during certain periods.

This text is unique in that it can be clearly dated to the rule of King Jonathan. Three columns of script are preserved, one on the top and two below. The upper column and the lower left column are incomplete. The leather is torn along the lower third of the right margin. A tab of untanned leather, 2.9 by 2.9 centimeters (1⅛ by 1⅛ inches), folds over the right edge above the tear. A leather thong, remains of which were found threaded through the middle of the tab, probably tied the rolled-up scroll (see catalog nos. 34 and 35 and page 139). The form of the tab—probably part of a fastening—seems to indicate that the extant text was at the beginning of the scroll, which was originally longer. Differences between the script of column A and that of B and C may indicate that the document is not the work of a single scribe.

This small manuscript contains two distinct parts. The first, column A, presents fragments of a psalm of praise to God. The second, columns B and C, bears a prayer for the welfare of King Jonathan and his kingdom. In column A lines 8–10 are similar to a verse in Psalm 154, preserved in the Psalms Scroll (11QPsa, Plate XVIII) exhibited here (catalog no. 4). This hymn, which was not included in the biblical Book of Psalms, is familiar, however, from the tenth-century Syriac Psalter.

Reference

Eshel, E., H. Eshel, and A. Yardeni. "A Qumran Scroll Containing Part of Psalm 154 and a Prayer for the Welfare of King Jonathan and His Kingdom," *Israel Exploration Journal* 42 (1992): 199–229.

2

PRAYER FOR
KING JONATHAN
TEFILLAH LI-SHLOMO
SHEL YONATAN
HA-MELEKH
תפילה לשלומו
4Q448
Copied 103–76 B.C.E.
17.8 × 9.5 cm
(7 × 3¾ in.)

Column A

1. Praise the Lord, a Psalm [of
2. You loved as a fa[ther(?)
3. you ruled over [
4. *vac* [
5. and your foes were afraid
    (or: will fear)[
6. . . . the heaven [
7. and to the depths of the sea [
8. and upon those who glorify
    him [
9. the humble from the hand
    of adversaries [
10. Zion for his habitation,
    ch[ooses

Column C

1. because you love Isr[ael
2. in the day and until evening [
3. to approach, to be [
4. Remember them for blessing[
5. on your name, which is called [
6. kingdom to be blessed [
7.]for the day of war [
8. to King Jonathan [
9.

Column B

1. holy city
2. for king Jonathan
3. and all the congregation
    of your people
4. Israel
5. who are in the four
6. winds of heaven
7. peace be (for) all
8. and upon your kingdom
9. your name be blessed

*Transcription and translation by
E. Eshel, H. Eshel, and A. Yardeni*

Column A

1. הללויה מזמו]ר ל

2. אהבת כא]

3. סרות על]

4. *vac*

5. ויראו מסנ]איך

6. רבים השמי]ם

7. ולתהום ים]

8. ועל מפארו]

9. עני מיד צרים]

10. משכנו בציון ב]

Column C

1. באהבתך אתיס

2. ביום ועד ערב מ...]

3. לקרוב להיות ב]

4. פקדם לברכה...]

5. על שמך שנקרא]

6. ממלכה להבר]ך

7. ל ום מלחמה]

8. ליונתן המל]ך

9. מת] [מת]

Column B

1. עיר קדש

2. על יונתן המלך

3. וכל קהל עמך

4. ישראל

5. אשר בארבע

6. רוחות שמים

7. יהי שלום כלם

8. ועל ממלכתך

9. יתברך שמך

3
LEVITICUS
VA-YIKRA
ויקרא
*11Q1 (PaleoLev)
Copied late second
century–early first
century B.C.E.
10.9 × 100.2 cm
(4¼ × 39½ in.)*

Inscribed in this scroll are parts of the final chapters (22–27) of Leviticus. It is the lowermost portion (approximately one-fifth of the original height) of the final six columns of the original manuscript. Eighteen small fragments also belong to this scroll. The additional fragments of this manuscript are from preceding chapters: Lev. 4, 10, 11, 13, 14, 16, 18–22.

The text is similar to the Masoretic text, the traditional text of the Hebrew Bible, and it proves that little change occurred over the centuries. The paleo-Hebrew script here seems to be just one manifestation of conservative traits that survived through generations and perhaps resurfaced in the Hasmonean era. Hasmonean coinage of the first century B.C.E. bears similar script. Noteworthy in the scroll is the habit often observed in paleo-Hebrew script of breaking off words at the end of lines. Also characteristic is the placement of the *vav* in open spaces between paragraphs, when the new paragraph should have begun with that letter (line 2 of Hebrew transcription).

A single scribe penned the text on the grain side of the skin in an inconsistent hand, at times patient with his task, at times careless. Both vertical and horizontal lines were drawn. The vertical lines aligned the columns and margins; the horizontal lines served as guidelines from which the scribe suspended his letters. Dots were used to indicate spaces between words. This scroll was discovered in 1956, when a group of Ta'amireh Bedouin happened on Cave 11, but it was first unrolled fourteen years later, at the Israel Museum in Jerusalem.

Reference

Freedman, D. N., and K. A. Mathews. *The Paleo-Hebrew Leviticus Scroll*. Winona Lake, Indiana, 1985.

Lev. 23:22–29

1. ²²[. . . edges of your field, or] gather [the gleanings of your harvest; you shall leave them for the poor and the stranger: I the LO]RD [am]

2. your God.

3. ²³The LORD spoke to Moses saying: ²⁴Speak to the Israelite people thus: In the seventh month

4. on the first day of the month, you shall observe complete rest, a sacred occasion commemorated with loud blasts.

5. ²⁵You shall not work at your occupations; and you shall bring an offering by fire to the LORD.

6. ²⁶The LORD spoke to Moses saying: ²⁷Mark, the tenth day of this seventh month is the Day

7. of Atonement. It shall be a sacred occasion for you: you shall practice self-denial, and you shall bring an offering

8. by fire to the LORD; ²⁸you shall do no work throughout that day. For

9. [it is a Day of Atonement on which] expiation is made on your behalf [before the LO]RD your God. ²⁹Indeed, any person who

Translation from Tanakh: A New Translation of the Holy Scriptures According to the Traditional Hebrew Text, *p. 192. Philadelphia, 1985.*

1. ‏[..... ....[רכ]....[תלקט] ....[תמ]..[נ]..[.]יה[...]

2. ‏[..]היכם. ו

3. ‏ידבר.יהוה.אל.משה.לאמר.דבר.אל.בני.ישראל.לאמר.בחדש.השב

4. ‏עי.באחד.לחדש.יהיה.לכמ.שבתון.זכרונ.תרועה.מקרא.קדש.ב

5. ‏ל.מלאכת.עבדה.לא.תעשו.והקרבתמ.אשה.ליהוה.

6. ‏וידבר.יהוה.אל.משה.לאמר.אב.בעשור.לחדש.השבעי.הזה.יומ

7. ‏הכפרימ.הוא.מקרא.קדש.יהיה.לכמ.ועניתמ.א[..]נפשתיכמ.והקרב

8. ‏ת[..]אשה[.]ליהוה.וכל.מלאכה.לא   תעשו.בעצמ.היומ.הזה.כי.יו

9. ‏[..... .....[וא].[.]לכפר.עליכמ.לפ[...]יה[..]אלהיכמ.כי.כל.הנפש.אשר

LEVITICUS
VA-YIKRA

4

PSALMS

TEHILLIM

תהילים

11QPs

Copied ca. 30–50 C.E.

18.5 × 86 cm

(7¼ × 33¾ in.)

This impressive scroll is a liturgical collection of psalms and hymns, comprising parts of forty-one biblical psalms (chiefly from chapters 101–50), in noncanonical sequence and with variations in detail. It also presents apocryphal psalms (previously unknown hymns dealing with the future) as well as a prose passage about the psalms composed by King David: "... And the total was 4,050. All these he composed through prophecy, which was given him from before the Most High" (11QPsᵃ 27:10–11).

One of the longer texts from Qumran, it was found in 1956 in Cave 11 and unrolled in 1961. Its surface is the thickest of any of the scrolls—it may be of calfskin rather than sheepskin, which was the common writing material at Qumran. The writing is on the grain side. The scroll contains twenty-eight incomplete columns of text, six of which are displayed here (cols. 14–19). Each of the preserved columns contains fourteen to eighteen lines; it is clear that six to seven lines are lacking at the bottom of each column.

The scroll's script is of fine quality, with the letters carefully drawn in the Jewish book-hand style of the Herodian period. The Tetragrammaton (the four-letter divine name) is inscribed in the paleo-Hebrew script, which is also used in the Leviticus scroll. On paleographic grounds the manuscript is dated between 30 and 50 C.E.

Reference

Sanders, J. A. *The Psalms Scroll of Qumrân Cave 11 (11QPsᵃ)*. Discoveries in the Judaean Desert, IV. Oxford, 1965.

Column 19: Plea for Deliverance (A Noncanonical Psalm)

1. Surely a maggot cannot praise thee nor a grave worm recount thy loving-kindness.

2. But the living can praise thee, even those who stumble can laud thee. In revealing

3. thy kindness to them and by thy righteousness thou dost enlighten them. For in thy hand is the soul of every

4. living thing; the breath of all flesh hast thou given. Deal with us, o LORD,

5. according to thy goodness, according to thy great mercy, and according to thy many righteous deeds. The LORD

6. has heeded the voice of those who love his name and has not deprived them of his loving-kindness.

7. Blessed be the LORD, who executes righteous deeds, crowning his saints

8. with loving-kindness and mercy. My soul cries out to praise thy name, to sing high praises

9. for thy loving deeds, to proclaim thy faithfulness—of praise of thee there is no end. Near death

10. was I for my sins, and my iniquities have sold me to the grave; but thou didst save me,

11. o LORD, according to thy great mercy, and according to thy many righteous deeds. Indeed have I

12. loved thy name, and in thy protection have I found refuge. When I remember thy might my heart

13. is brave, and upon thy mercies do I lean. Forgive my sin, o LORD,

14. and purify me from my iniquity. Vouchsafe me a spirit of faith and knowledge, and let me not be dishonored

15. in ruin. Let not Satan rule over me, nor an unclean spirit; neither let pain nor the evil

16. inclination take possession of my bones. For thou, o LORD, art my praise, and in thee do I hope

17. all the day. Let my brothers rejoice with me and the house of my father, who are astonished by the graciousness . . .

18. [   ] For e[ver] I will rejoice in thee.

Transcription and translation by J. A. Sanders

.10 הייתי בחטאי ועוונותי לשאול מכרוני ותצילני

.11 𐤉𐤄𐤅𐤄 כרוב רחמיכה וכרוב צדקותיכה גם אני את

.12 שמכה אהבתי ובצלכה חסיתי בזוכרי עוזכה יתקף

.13 לבי ועל חסדיכה אני נסמכתי סלחה 𐤉𐤄𐤅𐤄 לחטאתי

.14 וטהרני מעווני רוח אמונה ודעת חונני אל אתקלה

.15 בעווה אל תשלט בי שטן ורוח טמאה מכאוב ויצר

.16 רע אל ירשו בעצמי כי אתה 𐤉𐤄𐤅𐤄 שבחי ולכה קויתי

.17 כול היום ישמחו אחי עמי ובית אבי השוממים בחונכה

.18 [   ]לם אשמחה בכה

1. כי לוא רמה תודה לכה ולוא תספר חסדכה תולעה

2. חי חי   יודה לכה יודו לכה כול מוטטי רגל בהודיעכה

3. חסדכה להמה וצדקתכה תשכילם כי בידכה נפש כול

4. חי נשמת כול   בשר אתה נתתה עשה עמנו יהוה

5. כטובכה כרוב רחמיכה וכרוב צדקותיכה שמע

6. יהוה בקול אוהבי שמו ולוא עזב חסדו מהמה

7. ברוך יהוה עושה צדקות מעטר חסידיו

8. חסד ורחמים שאנה נפשי להלל שׁמכה אֶת להודות ברנה

9. חסדיכה להגיד אמונתכה לתהלתכה אין חקר למות

45

5
HOSEA COMMENTARY
PESHER HOSHE'A
פשר הושע
4Q166 (4QpHos^a)
Copied late first
century B.C.E.
17.5 × 16.8 cm
(6⅞ × 6⅝ in.)

The text of this scroll is a commentary *(pesher)* on the biblical verses of Hosea 2:8–14. Both eschatological (thoughts about the end of days) and historical allusions are used in interpreting the biblical text. The verse analogizes the relation of God, the husband, to Israel, the unfaithful wife. In the commentary the unfaithful ones have been led astray by "the man of the lie." The affliction befalling those led astray is famine. Although this famine could be a metaphor, it may well be a reference to an actual drought referred to in historical sources.

The manuscript shown here is the larger of two unrelated fragments of the Hosea Commentary found in Cave 4. The script, which is identical to that of a commentary on Psalms, belongs to the rustic, semiformal type of the Herodian era.

References

Allegro, J. M. *Qumrân Cave 4: I (4Q158–4Q186).* Discoveries in the Judaean Desert, V. Oxford, 1968.

Horgan, M. *Pesharim: Qumran Interpretations of Biblical Books.* Washington, 1979.

Hos. 2:10–14

1. ¹⁰[SHE DID NOT KNOW THAT] I MYSELF HAD GIVEN HER THE GRAIN
   [AND THE WINE]

2. [AND THE OIL, AND] (THAT) I HAD SUPPLIED [SILVER] AND GOLD
   {....} (WHICH) THEY MADE [INTO BAAL. The interpretation of it is]

3. that [they] ate [and] were satisfied, and they forgot God who [had fed
   them, and all]

4. his commandments they cast behind them, which he had sent to them
   [by]

5. his servants the prophets. But to those who led them astray they listened,
   and they honored them [   ]

6. and as if they were gods, they fear them in their blindness.

7. *vac*

8. ¹¹THEREFORE, I SHALL TAKE BACK MY GRAIN AGAIN IN ITS TIME AND
   MY WINE [IN ITS SEASON,]

9. AND I SHALL WITHDRAW MY WOOL AND MY FLAX FROM COVERING
   [HER NAKEDNESS.]

10. ¹²I SHALL NOW UNCOVER HER PRIVATE PARTS IN THE SIGHT OF [HER]
    LO[VERS AND]

11. NO [ONE] WILL WITHDRAW HER FROM MY HAND.

12. The interpretation of it is that he smote them with famine and with
    nakedness so that they became a disgra[ce]

13. and a reproach in the sight of the nations on whom they had leaned for
    support, but they

14. will not save them from their afflictions. ¹³AND I SHALL PUT AN END TO
    ALL HER JOY,

15. [HER] PIL[GRIMAGE,] HER [NEW] MOON, AND HER SABBATH, AND ALL
    HER FEASTS. The interpretation of it is that

16. they make [the fe]asts go according to the appointed times of the nation.
    And [all]

17. [joy] has been turned for them into mourning.
    ¹⁴AND I SHALL MAKE DESOLATE [HER VINE]

18. [AND HER FIG TREE,] OF WHICH SHE SAID, "THEY ARE THE HIRE
    [THAT MY LOVERS HAVE GIVEN] ME."

19. AND I SHALL MAKE THEM A FOREST, AND THE W[ILD BEAST OF THE
    FIELD] WILL DEVOUR THEM.

Transcription and translation by M. Horgan

1. [לוא ידעה כיא] אנוכי נתתי לה הדגן [והתירוש]

2. [והיצהר וכסף] הרביתי וזהב ... עשו [לבעל פשרו]

3. אשר [אכלו וי]שבעו וישכחו את אל המ[אכלם ואת כול]

4. מצוותיו השליכו אחרי גום אשר שלח אליהם [ביד]

5. עבדיו הנביאים ולמתעיהם שמעו ויכבדום [

6. וכאלים יפחדו מהם בעורונם [   ]

7. vac

8. לכן אשוב ולקחתי דגני בעתו ותירושי [במועדו]

9. והצלתי צמרי ופישתי מלכסות את [ערותה]

10. ועתה אגלה את נבלותה לעיני מאה[ביה ואיש]

11. לוא יצילנה מידי

12. פשרו אשר הכם ברעב ובערום להיות לקלו[ן]

13. וחרפה לעיני הגואים אשר נשענו עליהם והמה

14. לוא יושיעום מצרותיהם והשבתי כול משושה

15. ח[גנה חד]שה ושבתה וכול מועדיה פשרו אשר

16. [את המו]עדות יוליכו במועדי הגואים   ו[כול]

17. [שמחה] נהפכה להם לאבל והשמותי [גפנה]

18. [ותאנתה] אשר אמרה אתנם הם לי [אשר נתנו]

19. [לי מאהב]י ושמתים ליער ואכלתם ח[ית השדה]

48

6

COMMUNITY RULE

SEREKH HA-YAḤAD

סרך היחד

4Q258 (Sᵈ)

*Copied late first
century* B.C.E.–
early first century C.E.

8.8 × 21.5 cm

(3⁷⁄₁₆ × 8⁷⁄₁₆ in.)

Originally known as the Manual of Discipline, the Community Rule *(Serekh ha-Yaḥad)* contains regulations ordering the life of the members of the *yaḥad,* the group within the Judean Desert sect that chose to live communally. The strict rules of conduct they adopted for themselves formed the basis for the observance of the commandments of the Torah as the will of God. These commandments, however, are not cited in this scroll. The rules of conduct, which are accompanied by admonitions and punishments to be imposed on violators, deal with the manner of joining the group, the relations between the members, their way of life, and their beliefs. The sect divided humanity between the righteous and the wicked and asserted that human nature and everything that happens in the world are irrevocably predestined. The scroll ends with songs of praise to God.

A complete copy of the scroll, eleven columns in length, was found in Cave 1. Ten fragmentary copies were recovered in Cave 4, and a small section was found in Cave 5. The large number of manuscripts attests to the importance of this text for the sect. The manuscript shown here is the longest of the versions of this text found in Cave 4; it differs from the Cave 1 manuscript in that it is formulated in a more concise fashion.

Paleographic study of the Community Rule scroll indicates that it is in Herodian bookhand, whereas the complete scroll from Cave 1 is probably from the earlier part of the Hasmonean period.

Reference

Qimron, E. "A Preliminary Publication of 4QSᵈ Columns VII–VIII" (in Hebrew). *Tarbiz* 60 (1991): 435–37.

And according to his insight he shall admit him. In this way both his love and his hatred. No man shall argue or quarrel with the men of perdition. He shall keep his council in secrecy in the midst of the men of deceit and admonish with knowledge, truth and righteous commandment those of chosen conduct, each according to his spiritual quality and according to the norm of time. He shall guide them with knowledge and instruct them in the mysteries of wonder and truth in the midst of the members of the community, so that they shall behave decently with one another in all that has been revealed to them. That is the time for studying the Torah (lit. clearing the way) in the wilderness. He shall instruct them to do all that is required at that time, and to separate from all those who have not turned aside from all deceit.

These are the norms of conduct for the Master in those times with respect to his loving and to his everlasting hating of the men of perdition in a spirit of secrecy. He shall leave to them property and wealth and earnings like a slave to his lord, (showing) humility before the one who rules over him. He shall be zealous concerning the Law and be prepared for the Day of Revenge.

He shall perform the will [of God] in all his deeds and in all strength as He has commanded. He shall freely delight in all that befalls him, and shall desire nothing except God's will. . . .

Transcription and translation by E. Qimron

1. ולפי שכלו להגישו וכן אהבתו עם שנאתו ואשר לא יוכיח איש ולא
יתרובב עם אנשי ה(דע)[שח]ת

2. ולסתר עצתו בתוך אנשי העול ולהוכיח דעת אמת ומשפט צדק
לבחירי דרך איש כרוחו וכתכון

3. העת ל[והנחות]ם בדעה וכן להשכילם ברזי פלא ואמת בתוך אנשי
היחד להלך תמים איש את

4. [רעהו בכל] הנגלה להם היא עת פנות הדרך למדבר [ו]להשכילם
בכל הנמצא לעשות בעת

5. [הזאת והבדל] מכל איש אשר לא הסיר דרכו מכול עול   ואלה
תכוני הדרך למשכיל בעת[ים]

6. [האלה לאהבתו עם] שנאתו שנאת עולם עם אנשי השחת ברוח
הסתר ולעזוב למו הון ובצע

7. [ועמל כעבד למוש]ל בו וענוה לפני הרודה בו ולהיות איש מקנא
לחוק ועתי ליום [נקם לעשות]

8. [רצון בכל משלח כפים ובכ]ל ממשלו כאש[ר צוה וכ]ל הנעשה בו
ירצה בנדבה וזולת רצון [אל]

7
SOME TORAH
PRECEPTS
MIQṢAT MAʿASE
HA-TORAH
מקצת מעשי התורה
4Q396 (MMTᶜ)
Copied late first
century B.C.E.–
early first century C.E.
Fragment A: 8 × 12.9 cm
(3⅛ × 5 in.)
Fragment B: 4.3 × 7 cm
(1¹¹⁄₁₆ × 2¾ in.)
Fragment C: 9.1 ×
17.4 cm (3⁹⁄₁₆ × 6⅞ in.)

This scroll is a sectarian polemical document, of which six incomplete manuscripts have been discovered. Together, these fragments provide a composite text of about 130 lines, which probably cover two-thirds of the original. The initial part of the text is completely lacking. The scroll is commonly referred to as MMT, an abbreviation of its Hebrew name, *Miqṣat Maʿase ha-Torah,* which appears in the epilogue.

The document, apparently in letter form, is unique in language, style, and content. Using linguistic and theological considerations, the original text has been dated as one of the earliest works of the Qumran library.

Apparently it consisted of four sections: (1) the opening formula, now lost; (2) a calendar of 364 days; (3) a list of more than twenty rulings in religious law *(Halakhot),* most of which are peculiar to the sect; and (4) an epilogue that deals with the separation of the sect from the multitude of the people and attempts to persuade the addressee to adopt the sect's legal views. The *Halakhot* are the core of the letter; the remainder of the text is merely the framework. The calendar, although a separate section, was probably also related to the sphere of *Halakhah.* These *Halakhot* deal chiefly with the Temple and its ritual. The author states that disagreement on these matters caused the sect to secede from Israel.

Because the beginning of the text is lost, the identities of both the author and the addressee are missing. However, a commentary *(pesher)* to Psalm 37 relates that the "teacher of righteousness" conveyed a letter to his opponent, the "wicked priest." This may well be a reference to this document, which is addressed to "the leader of Israel."

In general, the script belongs to the semiformal tradition of Herodian times. It is noteworthy that several letters, formal and semiformal, exhibit early and late typological forms at the same time. The majority of the manuscripts are inscribed on parchment, although several papyrus fragments also have survived.

References

Qimron, E., and J. Strugnell. *Qumran Cave 4: V. Miqṣat Maʿase ha-Torah.* Discoveries in the Judaean Desert, X. Oxford, 1994.

Sussmann, Y. "The History of *Halakha* and the Dead Sea Scrolls—Preliminary Observations on Miqṣat Maʿase Ha-Torah (4QMMT)" (in Hebrew), *Tarbiz* 59 (1990): 11–76.

1. until sunset on the eighth day. And concerning [the impurity] of

2. the [dead] person we are of the opinion that every bone, whether it

3. has its flesh on it or not—should be (treated) according to the law of the dead or the slain.

4. And concerning the mixed marriages that are being performed among the people, and they are sons of holy [seed],

5. as is written, Israel is holy. And concerning his (Israel's) [clean] animal

6. it is written that one must not let it mate with another species, and concerning his clothes [it is written that they should not]

7. be of mixed stuff; and one must not sow his field and vineyard with mixed species.

8. Because they (Israel) are holy, and the sons of Aaron are [most holy.]

9. But you know that some of the priests and [the laity intermingle]

10. [And they] adhere to each other and pollute the holy seed

11. as well as their (i.e., the priests') own [seed] with corrupt women. Since [the sons of Aaron should . . .]

Transcription and translation by J. Strugnell and E. Qimron

1. עד בוא השמש ביום השמיני ועל [טמאת נפש]

2. האדם אנחנו אומרים שכול עצם ש[היא חסרה]

3. ושלמה כמשפט המת או החלל הוא vac

4. ועל הזונות הנעסה בתוך העם והמה ב[ני זרע]

5. קדש משכתוב קודש ישראל ועל בה[מתו הטהורה]

6. כתוב שלוא לרבעה כלאים ועל לבושו כתוב שלוא]

7. יהיה שעטנז ושלוא לזרוע שדו וכ[רמו כלאים]

8. [ב]גלל שהמה קדושים ובני אהרון ק[דושי קדושים]

9. [וא]תם יודעים שמקצת הכהנים וה[עם מתערבים]

10. [והם] מתוככים ומטמאי[ם] את זרע [הקודש ואף]

11. את [זרע]ם עם הזונות כ[י לבני אהרון   [

56

8

CALENDRICAL
DOCUMENT
MISHMAROT
משמרות
4Q321 (Mishmarot Bᵃ)
Copied ca. 50–25 B.C.E.
13.4 × 21.1 cm
(5¼ × 8¼ in.)

Among the numerous fragments of calendrical documents from Qumran, some, like this one from Cave 4, have distinctive features. Two special nights in every month of the lunar calendar of 354 days, which the wider Jewish community embraced, are listed in order, in a cycle of six years, that is, over seventy-two months: the night following that of the full moon in the middle of the month, when the moon begins to wane, and the night of the moon's total eclipse at the end of the month. While the first of these nights bears no specific designation, the other is denoted *duqah* or *duqo(h),* a term for the moon's thinness.

The dark, and therefore ominous, nights are dated by attaching them to days that precede them in the solar cycle of 364 days to which the Qumran community adhered. At the same time they are also synchronized with the concurrent days of the week of service in the Jerusalem Temple of a specific priestly watch.

It appears that these rosters, penned in a late Hasmonean or early Herodian bookhand, were intended to provide the members of the New Covenant with a timetable for abstaining from important activities on the days before the dark phases of the moon's waning and eclipse. In contrast, rabbinic tradition puts a premium on the moon's bright phases: the night of the new moon at the beginning of the month and the night of the full moon in its middle.

References

Jaubert, A. "Le Calendrier de Jubilés et de la Secte de Qumrân: Ses origines Bibliques," *Vetus Testamentum* 3 (1953): 250–64.

Talmon, S. "The Calendar of the Judean Covenanteers." In *The World of Qumran from Within: Collected Studies,* pp. 147–85. Jerusalem, 1989.

Talmon, S., and I. Knohl. "A Calendrical Scroll from Qumran Cave IV—Miš Ba (4Q321)" (in Hebrew), *Tarbiz* 60 (1991): 505–21.

1. [on the first {day} in {the week of} Jedaiah {which falls} on the tw]elfth in it {the seventh month}. On the second {day} in {the week of} Abia[h {which falls} on the twenty-f]ifth in the eighth {month}; and *duqah* {is} on the third] {day}

2. [in {the week of} Miyamin {which falls} on the twelfth] in it {the eighth month}. On the third {day} in {the week of} Jaqim {which falls} on the twen[ty-fourth in the ninth {month}; and *duqah* {is} on the fourth] {day}

3. [in {the week of} Shekaniah {which falls} on the eleven]th in it {the ninth month}. On the fifth {day} in {the week of} Immer {which falls} on the twe[n]ty-third in the te[nth {month}; and *duqah* {is} on the sixth {day} in {the week of Jeshbeab] {which falls}

4. [on the tenth in] it {the tenth month}. On the [si]xth {day} in {the week of} Jeḥezkel {which falls} on the twenty-second in the eleventh month [and *duqah* {is on the} Sabbath in {the week of} Petaḥah] {which falls}

5. [on the ninth in it {the eleventh month}]. On the first {day} in {the week of} Joiarib {which falls} on the t[w]enty-second in the twelfth month; and [*duqah* {is} on the second {day}] in {the week of} Delaiah] {which falls}

6. [on the ninth in it] {the twelfth month}. *vac* The] se[cond] {year}: The first {month}. On the sec[on]d {day} in {the week of} Malakiah {which falls} on the tw[entieth in it {the first month}; and *duqah*] {is}

7. [on the third {day} in {the week of} Harim {which falls} on the seventh] in it {the first month}. On the fou[r]th {day} in {the week of} Jeshua {which falls} [on] the twentieth in the second {month}; and [*duqah* {is} on the fifth {day} in {the week of} Haqqoṣ {which falls} on the seventh]

8. [in it {the second month}. On the fifth {day} in {the week of} Ḥuppah {which falls} on the nine]teenth in the third {month}; and *duqa*[*h*] {is} on the six[th {day} in {the week of} Happisses {which falls}

Translation and transcription by S. Talmon and I. Knohl

1. ‏[באחד בידעיה בשני]ם עשר בוא בשנים באבי[ה בחמישה]
‏ועש[רים בשמיני ודוקה בשלושה]

2. ‏[במימין בשנים עשר] בוא בשלושה ביקים בא[רבעה ועשרים
‏בתשיעי ודוקה בארבעה]

3. ‏[בשכניה בעשתי ע]שר בוא בחמשה באמר בשלושה וע[ש]רים
‏בעש[ירי ודוקה בששה בישבאב]

4. ‏[בעשרה בו]א ב[ש]שה ביחזקאל בשנים ועשרים בעשתי עשר
‏החודש ו]דוקה שבת בפתחה]

5. ‏[בתשעה בוא] באחד ביוייריב בשנו[י]ם ועשרים בשנים עשר החודש
‏ו]דוקה בשנים בדליה]

6. ‏[בתשעה בוא vac השנה ה]שנ[ית] הראשון בש[נ]ים במלאכה
‏בע]שרים בוא ודוקה]

7. ‏[בשלושה בחרים בשבעה] בוא בארבע[ע]ה בישוע [ב]עשרים בשני
‏ו]דוקה בחמשה בקוץ בשבעה]

8. ‏[בוא בחמשה בחופה בתשעה] עשר בשלישי ודוק[ה] בשש[ה]
‏בא[ל]ישי]ב ב[ש]שה [בוא שב]ת בפצץ

One of the most important apocryphic works of the Second Temple period is Enoch. According to the biblical narrative (Gen. 5:21–24), Enoch lived 365 years (far less than the other antediluvian patriarchs) and "walked with God; then he was no more for God took him."

Rabbinic sources and pseudepigraphic literature (books not included in the Hebrew Old Testament) attach many tales and legends to this figure. He is all wise, knowing the secrets of the universe and being the source of information for natural and supernatural occurrences. The fullest portrait of Enoch emerges in 1 Enoch, a work preserved in its entirety only in Geʻez (Old Ethiopic).

The Book of Enoch is the earliest of the pseudepigraphic books. It is quoted in Jubilees and the Testaments of the Twelve Patriarchs, is referred to in the New Testament (Jude 1:14), and was used by the author of the Damascus Document.

The original language of most of this work was, in all likelihood, Aramaic, which was lost in antiquity. Portions of a Greek translation were discovered in Egypt, and quotations were known from the church fathers. The discovery of the texts from Qumran Cave 4 has finally provided parts of the Aramaic original, covering 1 Enoch. The Qumran text includes the Book of Giants, previously known from Manichaean adaptations in a variety of languages.

The Qumran manuscripts of Enoch have been dated paleographically from the early second century to the end of the first century B.C.E. The two texts presented here are from 4QEnᵃ, which is attributed to the first half of the second century B.C.E.

In the fragment exhibited, humankind is called on to observe how unchanging nature follows God's will. In the first verse transcribed here, man is chastised for changing His work and transgressing. Further along, it states that humankind will be cursed for eternity. In the second verse, the Watchers saw the beautiful daughters of humankind and desired them for wives. They are bound together by oath, and the names of the twenty Chiefs of Ten, known from later tradition, are given. The lines presented here (13–16) tell about their taking wives and teaching them occult arts. The wives gave birth to giants, who wreaked destruction.

Reference

Milik, J. T. *The Books of Enoch: Aramaic Fragments of Qumran Cave 4.* Oxford, 1976.

9
ENOCH
ḤANOKH
חנוך
4Q201 (En arᵃ)
Copied ca. 200–150 B.C.E
Fragment A: 17.5 × 17.5 cm (6⅞ × 6⅞ in.)
Fragment B: 6.4 × 6.9 cm (2½ × 2¹¹⁄₁₆ in.)

En^a I ii

12. . . . But you have changed your works,
13. [and have not done according to his command, and tran]sgressed against him; (and have spoken) haughty and harsh words, with your impure mouths,
14. [against his majesty, for your heart is hard]. You will have no peace.

En^a I iii

13. [They (the leaders) and all . . . of them took for themselves]
14. wives from all that they chose and [they began to cohabit with them and to defile themselves with them];
15. and to teach them sorcery and [spells and the cutting of roots; and to acquaint them with herbs.]
16. And they become pregnant by them and bo[re (great) giants three thousand cubits high . . .]

Transcription by J. T. Milik, amended by J. C. Greenfield;
translation by J. C. Greenfield

En^a I ii

12.   ...ואנתן שניתן עבדכן

13.   [ולא תעבדון ממרה ותע]ברון עלוהי [ותמללון] רברבן וקשין
      בפום (!) טמתכן

14.   [על רבותה די קשה לבב]כן לת שלם לכן...

ENOCH
ḤANOKH

En^a I iii

13.   [אנון ו...כלהן נסבו להן]

14.   נשין מן כל די בחרו ו[שריו למנעל עליהן ולאסתאבה בהן]

15.   ולאלפה אנין חרשה ו[כשפה ומקטע שרשין ולאחויה להן עסבין]

16.   והויה בטנן מנהן ויל[דן גברין רמין תלתת אלפין אמה...]

10
WAR RULE
SEREKH
HA-MILḤAMAH
סרך המלחמה
4Q285 (SM)
Copied early first
century C.E.
4 × 5 cm (1½ × 2 in.)

This six-line fragment, written in a Herodian script of the first half of the first century C.E., refers to a Messiah from the Branch of David, to a judgment, and to a killing. The word והמיתו (line 4) could suggest "and the Prince of the Congregation, the Branch of David, will kill him," but the nonvocalized reading also allows for "and they killed the Prince." The text was therefore dubbed the "Pierced Messiah" text. The transcription and translation presented here support the "killing Messiah" interpretation, alluding to a triumphant Messiah (Is. 11:4).

References

Tabor, J. "A Pierced or Piercing Messiah?—The Verdict Is Still Out," *Biblical Archaeology Review* 18 (1992): 58–59.
Vermes, G. "The Oxford Forum for Qumran Research: Seminar on the Rule of War from Cave 4 (4Q285)," *Journal of Jewish Studies* 43 (Spring 1992): 85–90.

1.]Isaiah the prophet: [The thickets of the forest] will be cut [down
2. with an axe and Lebanon by a majestic one will f]all. And there shall come forth a shoot from the stump of Jesse [
3.]the Branch of David and they will enter into judgement with [
4.]and the Prince of the Congregation, the Bran[ch of David] will kill him [
5. by stroke]s and by wounds. And a Priest [of renown (?)] will command [
6. the s]lai[n] of the Kitti[m]

Transcription and translation by G. Vermes

WAR RULE

SEREKH

HA-MILḤAMAH

1.]ישעיהו הנביא ונוק[פו

2. י]פול ויצא חוטר מגזע ישי [

3.]צמח דויד ונשפטו את [

4.]והמיתו נשיא העדה צמ[ח דויד

5.]גם ובמחוללות וצוה כוהן [

6. ח]ללי[ן] כתיים [   ]ל[

II

ARAMAIC

APOCALYPSE

ברה די אל

4Q246

Copied end of first

century B.C.E.

14.1 × 8.8 cm

(5½ × 3½ in.)

This Aramaic text, similar to the apocalyptic section of the biblical book of Daniel, refers to a "Son of God" and "Son of the Most High," terms also used in the Gospels (e.g., Luke 1:32, 35). The interpretation of these terms is widely disputed by scholars—is this a reference to a historic ruling figure or to an apocalyptic sovereign who will establish the reign of God on earth?

Reference

Puech, E. *Qumran Cave 4: XVII. Parabiblical Texts, Part 3*. Discoveries in the Judaean Desert, XXII, pp. 165–84. Oxford, 1996.

Column 2

1. The son of God he will be proclaimed (or: proclaim himself) and the son of the Most High they will call him. Like the sparks

2. of the vision, so will be their kingdom. They will reign for years on

3. the earth and they will trample all. People will trample people (cf. Dan. vii 23) and one province another province

4. *vac* until the people of God will arise and all will rest from the sword.

5. Their (the people of God's) kingdom will be an eternal kingdom (cf. Dan. vii 27) and all their path will be in truth.

6. They will jud[ge] the earth in truth and all will make peace. The sword will cease from the earth

7. and all the provinces will pay homage to them. The Great God (cf. Dan. ii 45) is their helper.

8. He will wage war for them. He will give peoples into their hands and all of them (the peoples)

9. He will cast before them (the people of God). Their dominion will be an eternal dominion (Dan. vii 14) and all the boundaries of . . .

Transcription by E. Puech; translation by G. Vermes

Column 2

1. ברה די אל יתאמר ובר עליון יקרונה כזיקיא

2. די חזותא כן מלכותהן תהוה שני[ן] ימלכון על

3. ארעא וכלא ידשון עם לעם ומדינה למדי[נ]ה

4. *vac* עד יקו/ים עם אל וכלא ינו/יח מן חרב

5. מלכותה מלכות עלם וכל ארחתה בקשוט ידי[ן]

6. ארעא בקשט וכלא יעבד שלם חרב מן ארעא יסף

7. וכל מדינתא לה יסגדון אל רבא באילה

8. הוא ועבד לה קרב עממין ינתן בידה וכלהן

9. ירמה קדמוהי שלטנה שלטן עלם וכל תהומי

This fragmentary manuscript is part of a larger sapiential composition, poorly preserved in some fifty fragments in Cave 4.

The literary genre of the composition, with the repeated use of *ashré* (blessed), is reminiscent of several Old and New Testament works. Particularly striking is its similarity to the Beatitudes in "The Sermon on the Mount" (Matthew 5:3–12), but it has its counterparts in other contemporaneous texts as well.

E. Puech, the editor of the text, dates its original composition to the first half of the second century B.C.E.

Reference

Puech, E. *Qumran Cave 4: XVII. Texts Hébreux.* Discoveries in the Judaean
    Desert, XXV. Oxford, 1998.

12

BEATITUDES

. . . אשרי

4Q525

Copied second half

of first century B.C.E.

Fragment 2:

18.5 × 10.5 cm

(7½ × 4⅛ in.)

1. [Blessed is] ... with a pure heart
   and does not slander with his tongue.
   Blessed are those who hold to her (Wisdom's)
   precepts and do not hold
2. to the ways of iniquity.
   Blessed are those who rejoice in her,
   and do not burst forth in ways of folly.
3. Blessed are those who seek her with pure hands,
   and do not pursue her with a treacherous heart.
   Blessed is the man who has attained Wisdom, and walks
4. in the Law of the Most High.
   He directs his heart towards her ways,
   and restrains himself by her corrections,
   and always takes delight in her chastisements.
5. He does not forsake her when he sees distress,
   nor abandon her in time of strain.
   He will not forget her [on the day of] fear,
6. and will not despise [her] when his soul is afflicted.
   For always he will meditate on her,
   and in his distress he will consider [her?]

Transcription by E. Puech; translation by G. Vermes

1. בלב טהור ולוא רגל על לשונו *vac* אשרי תומכי חוקיה ולוא יתמוכו

2. בדרכי עולה *vac* אש[רי] הגלים בה ולוא יביעו בדרכי אולת *vac* אשרי דורשיה

3. בבור כפים ולוא ישחרנה בלב מרמה *vac* אשרי אדם השיג חוכמה ויתהלך *vac*

BEATITUDES

4. בתורת עליון ויכן לדרכיה לבו *vac* ויתאפק ביסוריה ובנגועיה ירצה תמ[י]ד

5. ולוא יטושנה בעוני מצר[יו/פו] ובעת צוקה לוא יעוזבנה ולוא ישכחנה [בימי / יום]פחד

6. ובענות נפשו לוא יגעל[נה *vac*]כי בה יהגה תמיד ובצרתו ישוחח [בה ובכו]ל

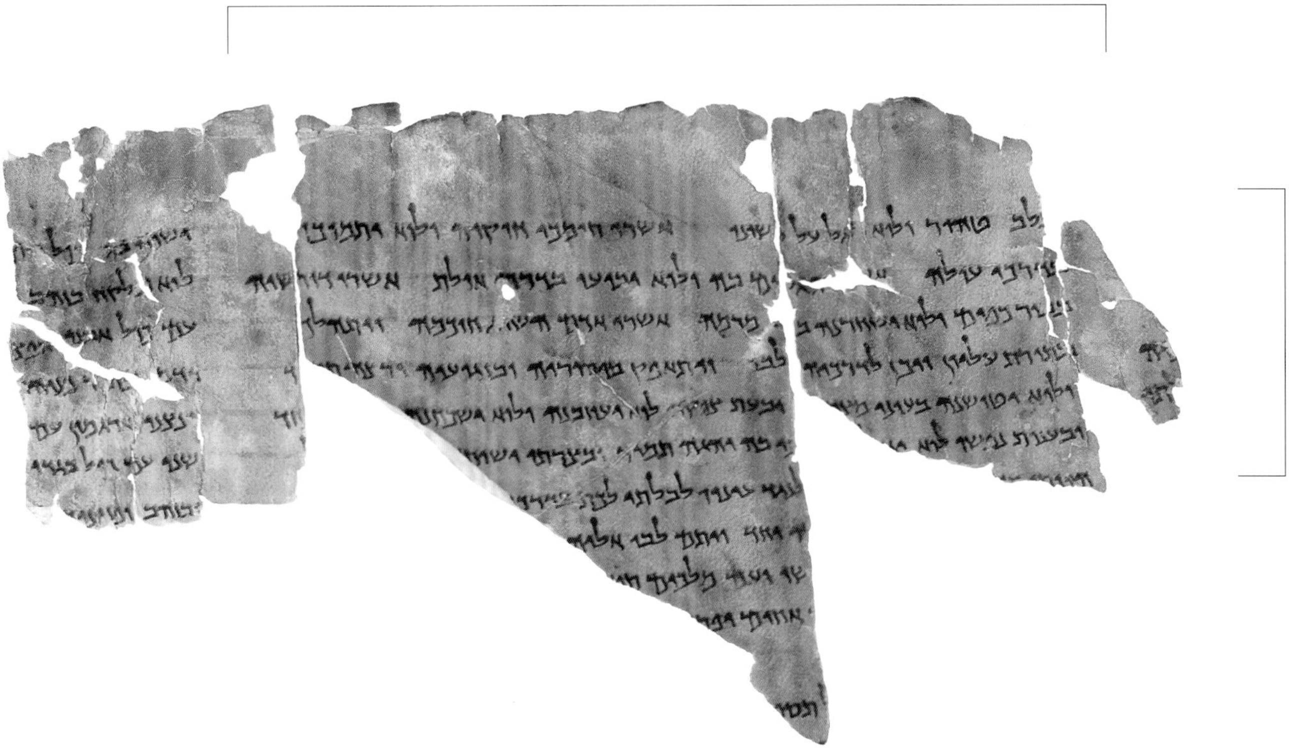

13
MESSIANIC
APOCALYPSE
ומתים יחיה
(On Resurrection)
4Q521
Copied early first
century B.C.E.
Fragments 2–3:
maximum 17.5 × 11 cm
(6⅞ × 4⅜ in.)

Eleven fragments of this text, as well as a number of tiny scraps, were retrieved from Cave 4 and recently published.

The name of this Hebrew composition derives from the term *Messiah* mentioned in line 1. The text deals with healing of the sick and resurrection of the dead, which will take place in God's kingdom. As opposed to previously published Qumranic works in which two Messiahs figured, this text refers to a single Messiah, reminiscent of the Christian messianic concept.

Reference

Puech, E. *Qumran Cave 4: XVII. Texts Hébreux.* Discoveries in the Judaean Desert, XXV. Oxford, 1998.

1. . . . [the hea]vens and the earth will listen to His Messiah,

2. and none therein will stray from the commandments of the holy ones.

3. Seekers of the Lord, strengthen yourselves in His service!

4. All you hopeful in (your) heart, will you not find the Lord in this?

5. For the lord will consider the pious (ḥasidim) and call the righteous by name.

6. Over the poor His spirit will hover and will renew the faithful with His power.

7. And he will glorify the pious on the throne of the eternal Kingdom.

8. He who liberates the captives, restores sight to the blind, straightens the b[ent] (Ps. cxlvi 7–8).

9. And f[or] ever I will clea[ve to the h]opeful and in His mercy . . .

10. And the fr[uit . . .] will not be delayed for anyone

11. And the Lord will accomplish glorious things which have never been as [He . . .]

12. For He will heal the wounded, and revive the dead and bring good news to the poor (Isa. lxi 1).

Transcription by E. Puech; translation by G. Vermes

1. ‏[כי הש]מים והארץ ישמעו למשיחו

2. ‏[וכל א]שר בם לוא יסוג ממצות קדושים

3. ‏התאמצו מבקשי אדני בעבדתו *vac*

4. ‏הלוא בזאת תמצאו את אדני כל המיחלים בלבם

5. ‏כי אדני חסידים יבקר וצדיקים בשם יקרא

6. ‏ועל ענוים רוחו תרחף ואמונים יחליף בכחו

7. ‏כי יכבד את חסידים על כסא מלכות עד

8. ‏מתיר אסורים פוקח עורים זוקף כפ[ופים]

9. ‏ול[ע]לם אדבק [במ]יחלים ובחסדו י[   ]

10. ‏ופר[י מעש]ה טוב לאיש לוא יתאחר

11. ‏ונכבדות שלוא היו יעשה אדני כאשר ד[בר]

12. ‏כי ירפא חללים ומתים יחיה ענוים יבשר

MESSIANIC
APOCALYPSE

14
Deuteronomy
דברים
4QDeut^n
Copied ca. 30–1 B.C.E.
45 × 7.1 cm
(17¾ × 2¾ in.)

This scroll consists of six columns, one of them partially preserved. Column 1, a separate sheet of leather, contains the text of Deut. 8:5–10; columns 2–6, a continuous sheet of leather, bear the text of Deut. 5:1–6:1, which includes the text of the Ten Commandments. It has been suggested that this selection of passages was prepared for liturgical purposes.

The manuscript is written in full orthography and is in the characteristic script of the Herodian period (second half of the first century B.C.E.).

Reference

Crawford, S. W. *Qumran Cave 4: IX. Deuteronomy, Joshua, Judges, Kings.* Discoveries in the Judaean Desert, XIV, pp. 117–28. Oxford, 1995.

I am the Lord your God who

1. brought you out of the land of Egypt, out of the house of bondage.
   You shall have no

2. other gods before me. You shall not make for yourself a graven image
   or any

3. likeness of any thing that is in heaven above, or that is on earth beneath,
   or that

4. is in the water under the earth; you shall not bow down to them
   or serve them;

5. for I the Lord your God am a jealous God,
   visiting the iniquity of the fathers upon

6. the children to the third and fourth generation of those who hate me,
   [   ] showing steadfast love to thousands

7. of those who love me and keep my commandments.
   You shall not take the name of the Lord your God

8. in vain; for the Lord will not hold him guiltless
   who takes his name in vain.

9. Observe the sabbath day, to keep it holy,
   as the Lord your God commanded you.

10. Six days you shall labor and do all your work;

11. but *on* the seventh day, the sabbath to the Lord your God,
    you shall do no work *in it,*

12. you, [   ] your son, [   ] your daughter, [   ] your manservant,
    or your maidservant, [   ] your ox, or your ass,

Transcription by S. White Crawford

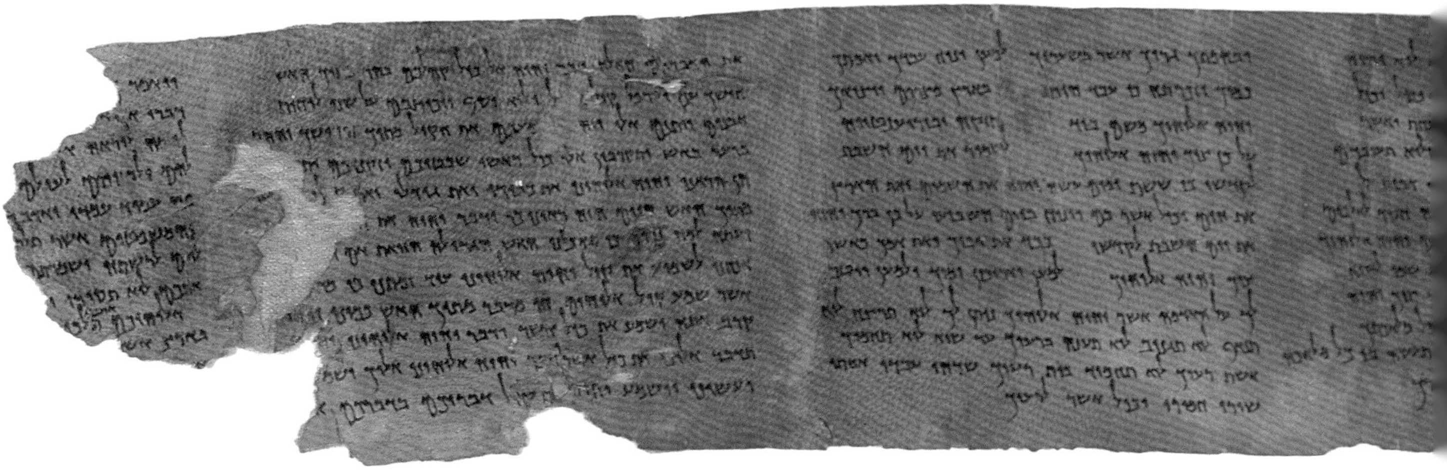

Deut. 5:6–14

1. הוצאתיך מארץ מצרים מבית עבדים לוא יהיה

2. לך אלוהים אחרים על פני לא תעשה לך פסל וכול

3. תמונה אשר בשמים ממעל ואשר בארץ מתחת ואשר

4. במים מתחת לארץ לוא תשתחוה להם ולוא תעובדם

5. כי אנוכי יהוה אלוהיך אל קנא פוקד עוון אבות על

6. בנים על שלשים ועל רבעים לשנאי עושה חסד לאלפים

7. לאוהבי ולשומרי מצוותי לוא תשא את שם יהוה אלוהיך

8. לשוא כי לוא ינקה יהוה את אשר ישא את שמו לשוא

9. שמור   את יום השבת לקדשו כאשר צוך יהוה

10. אלוהיך ששת ימים תעבוד ועשית את כול מלאכתך

11. וביום השביעי שבת ליהוה אלוהיך לוא תעשה בו כל מלאכה

12. אתה בנך בתך עבדך ואמתך שורך וחמורך

85

15
GREEK FRAGMENTS
7Q1–19
Copied first century
C.E./B.C.E.

Relatively few Greek manuscripts have been found in the Qumran caves. Most of them belong to ancient Greek scripture and show only minor deviations from the Septuagint text.

At the same time, several dozen minute fragments, published by the editors in 1962 as unidentifiable, have since received surprising attention. It has been hypothesized that they actually contain segments of some six New Testament writings: e.g., Mark 4:28 (7Q6i), Mark 6:52–53 (7Q5), and Acts 28:38 (7Q6ii). This identification has been questioned and heavily criticized.

Reference

Baillet, M., J. T. Milik, and R. de Vaux. *Les 'Petites Grottes' de Qumran.* Discoveries in the Judaean Desert, III. Oxford, 1962.

FROM THE QUMRAN RUIN

In the 1955 season of excavations at Qumran, three intact ceramic vessels containing 561 silver coins were found under a doorway between Levels Ib and II. The vessels were filled to the brim with coins, and the mouth of one of the vessels was covered with a palm-fiber stopper.

Père Roland de Vaux, excavator of Qumran, relied heavily on the coin evidence for his dating and interpretations of the various phases of the site. The early coins in the hoard were tetradrachms of Antiochus VII Sidetes and Demetrius II Nicator (136/135 to 127/126 B.C.E.), minted in Tyre, as well as six Roman Republican coins from the mid-first century B.C.E. The bulk of the hoard represents the autonomous continuation of the Seleucid mint: the well-known series of Tyrian *shekalim* and half-*shekalim,* minted from 126/125 B.C.E. onward. These are the same coins that were prescribed in the Temple for the poll tax and other payments (Tosefta. *Ketubot* 13, 20).

Two of the three hoard vessels are of a type otherwise unknown in the ceramic repertoire at Qumran. De Vaux suggested that this fact corroborated the information in the Community Rule, which relates that new adherents were to surrender their worldly goods to the treasurer of the community. The vessels' contents would then constitute the deposit of one or a number of new adherents. On the other hand, it should be noted that foundation deposits of coins—often under doorways—were common in antiquity.

Shown here are twenty-four Tyrian *shekalim* and half-*shekalim* minted between the years 103/102 and 10/9 B.C.E.

Donald T. Ariel

References
Meshorer, Y. *Ancient Jewish Coinage.* Dix Hills, N.Y., 1982.
Sharabani, M. "Monnaies de Qumrân au Musée Rockefeller de Jérusalem," *Revue Biblique* 87 (1980): 274–84.

16
HOARD OF COINS
24 silver coins
136/135 B.C.E.–10/9 B.C.E.
Diameter 1.9–2.8 cm
(¾–1⅛ in.)

The obverse shows the diademed head of Demetrius to the right. On the reverse is an eagle perched on a prow, at its shoulder a palm branch; in the left field is a club surmounted by the monogram of Tyre and the letters APE; in the right field are the letters AΣ̌ and the date ϜΠΡ (186 of the Seleucid era); between the eagle's legs is the symbol ⫪Р. Around all is the inscription ΒΑΣΙΛΕΩΣ ΔΗΜΗΤΡΙΟΥ (Of King Demetrius).

On the obverse of this coin is a laureate head of Melqarth (in his Hellenized form as Heracles) to the right. The reverse shows an eagle on a prow, a palm branch at its shoulder; in the left field is a club and the date ϘΘ (99 of the Tyrian era); in the right field is a monogram 𝕬; between the eagle's legs is the symbol ⌐. The inscription ΤΥΡΟΥ ΙΕΡΑΣ ΚΑΙ ΑΣΥΛΟΥ (Of holy, sanctuary-providing Tyre) encircles the coin.

16A
TETRADRACHM
OF DEMETRIUS II
Q65
127/126 B.C.E.
Diameter 2.7 cm (1 in.)

16B
TYRIAN SHEKEL
Q3
28/27 B.C.E.
Diameter 2.7 cm (1 in.)

Pottery, coins, and written material found at an archaeological site allow for the establishment of a relative and an absolute chronological and cultural framework. Consequently, the pottery found in the Dead Sea area disclosed many facets of the Qumran story.

The vessels shown here are representative of the finds from the immediate area of Qumran. Items from the surrounding caves and openings in the cliffs proved to be identical to those excavated at the Qumran site itself. It seems to have been a regional center—most likely a single pottery workshop supplied the entire area.

The repertory of ceramic finds from Qumran is limited and, apart from a large number of cylindrical scroll jars, consists chiefly of modest items of daily use: juglets, flasks, drinking cups, cooking pots, serving dishes, and bowls. A storeroom found during the excavation contained more than a thousand pottery items arranged by usage: vessels for cooking, serving, pouring, drinking, and dining.

References
De Vaux, R. *Archaeology and the Dead Sea Scrolls.* London, 1973.
Lapp, P. *Palestinian Ceramic Chronology, 200 B.C.–A.D. 70.* New Haven, 1961.

Some of the Dead Sea Scrolls were found by Bedouin shepherds in 1947 in cylindrical pottery jars of this type, which are unknown elsewhere. The discovery of these singular vessels in the Qumran excavations as well as in the caves, where they held scrolls, is considered by many to be convincing evidence of the link between the settlement and the caves. These jars, as well as the other pottery vessels recovered at Qumran, are probably of local manufacture.

17
JAR WITH LID
Pottery
KhQ 1474
First century B.C.E.–
first century C.E.
Lid: Height 5 cm (2 in.),
diameter 17.8 cm (7 in.).
Jar: Height 49.8 cm
(19½ in.), diameter
24 cm (9⅜ in.)

18
HERODIAN LAMP
Pottery with fiber wick
52.2
First century B.C.E.–
first century C.E.
Height 4.3 cm (1¹¹⁄₁₆
in.), length 10 cm (4 in.)

The earliest occurrences of this type of lamp were in strata associated with Herod's reign (37–4 B.C.E.). However, the dating of the lamp has been modified by recent excavations. A similar lamp type was uncovered in the Jewish Quarter of Jerusalem, in strata relating to the destruction of the Second Temple (70 C.E.), thus indicating a date later than was previously assumed.

The lamp's characteristic features are a circular wheel-made body, flat unmarked base, and large central filling hole. The spatulate nozzle was separately handformed and subsequently attached to the body. Traces of a palm-fiber wick were found in the lamp's nozzle.

Two inkwells were found at the Qumran excavations, this one of pottery and another of bronze. They were in the vicinity of a large table, which suggested to the site's excavators scribal activity in a scriptorium. It is feasible that many of the manuscripts were written or copied locally, although manuscripts of earlier date and other locations do occur.

This cylindrical pottery vessel has a flat base and a small, circular, rimmed opening at the top for dipping the pen and topping up the ink. This type of vessel also was found in excavations in Jerusalem.

19
INKWELL
Pottery
I.2179
Late first century B.C.E.–
early first century C.E.
Height 4.6 cm (1¾ in.),
diameter 3.9 cm (1½ in.)

20
PLATES

Pottery
KhQ 1591 a–o
First century B.C.E.–
first century C.E.
Height 2.6–5.5 cm
(1–2³⁄₁₆ in.),
diameter 13.6–16.4 cm
(13³⁄₈–6⁷⁄₁₆ in.)

Plates, bowls, and goblets were found in one of the rooms at Qumran, with dozens of vessels piled one on top of the other. This room probably served as a pantry near the assembly room, which may have served as a dining room.

The wheel-made plates are shallow, with a ring base and upright rim. The firing is metallic. Hundreds of plates were recovered, most of them complete, some with traces of soot.

This elongated, barrel-shaped jar has a ring base, a ribbed body, a very short wide neck, and two loop handles. The vessel was probably used to store provisions.

21
TWO-HANDLED JAR
Pottery
KhQ 1634
First century B.C.E.–
first century C.E.
Height 37.25 cm
(14½ in.), diameter
18.7 cm (7¼ in.)

22

JUG

Pottery

KhQ 1192

First century B.C.E.–
first century C.E.

Height 19.5 cm (7⅝ in.),
diameter 14 cm (5½ in.)

This globular jug has a ribbed body and a long, tapering neck ending in a splayed rim. A single-loop handle extends from the rim to the upper part of the body.

This flattened pot has a ribbed shoulder and a short, wide neck. The firing is metallic.

23
COOKING POT
Pottery
KhQ 1565
First century B.C.E.–
first century C.E.
Height 15 cm (5⅞ in.),
diameter 24 cm (9⅜ in.)

24

COOKING POT

Pottery

KhQ 2506

First century B.C.E.–
first century C.E.

Height 20.5 cm (8 in.),
diameter 26 cm (10¼ in.)

A globular-shaped design, this pot is similar to item no. 25 opposite. The surface of the body, from shoulder to base, is ribbed. Two ribbed handles span the vessel from the rim to the upper part of the shoulder. The firing is metallic. Traces of soot are discernible over the lower part.

25
COOKING POT
Pottery
KhQ 2506/a
First century B.C.E.–
first century C.E.
Height 22 cm (8⅝ in.),
diameter 23 cm (9 in.)

26

BOWLS

Pottery

KhQ 1601/a

First century B.C.E.–
first century C.E.

*Bowl A: Height 8.5 cm
(3⅜ in.), diameter
12.4 cm (4⅞ in.)*

*Bowl B: Height 9.2 cm
(3⅝ in.), diameter
13.5 cm (5⁵⁄₁₆ in.)*

Hemispherical in shape, these bowls have a ring base and an inverted rim.

27

GOBLETS

Pottery (stacked)

KhQ 1587 a–h

First century B.C.E.–
first century C.E.

*Height 26.5 cm
(10⁷⁄₁₆ in.), diameter
16 cm (6¼ in.)*

Found in a stack, these identical V-shaped drinking goblets are of fine ware. They were found in the pottery storeroom, excavated in the Qumran ruin.

Stone vessels, usually manufactured of easily workable, soft limestone, were common in the Jerusalem area in the late Second Temple period. They were abundant in Qumran in a variety of shapes and sizes and demonstrate expert workmanship.

The reason for their existence can be found in Jewish ritual law *(Halakhah)*. Stone—as opposed to pottery—does not become ritually unclean *(tamei)*. Jewish law maintains that pottery vessels that have become ritually unclean must be broken, never to be used again, whereas in similar circumstances stone vessels retain their ritual purity and need not be discarded (Mishnah. *Kelim* 10:11; *Parah* 3:2).

Widespread use of these stone vessels is particularly evident because of their discovery in the excavations of the Jewish Quarter in Jerusalem. Some of these vessels served the same functions as ceramic vessels, and some had particular shapes and functions. Although the raw material is common in Jerusalem, the cost of production was, no doubt, far greater than that of pottery. The flourishing manufacture of stone vessels came to an end in the wake of the destruction of the Second Temple (70 C.E.).

This large goblet-shaped vessel was produced on a lathe, probably in Jerusalem, and shows excellent craftsmanship. It is surprising that an ancient lathe was capable of supporting and working such a large and heavy stone block. The vessel may shed light on the shape of the *kallal* mentioned in the Talmudic sources—the vessel holding the purification ashes of the red heifer (Mishnah. *Parah* 3:3).

STONE VESSELS

28
LARGE GOBLET
Limestone
First century C.E.
Height 72 cm (28¼ in.),
diameter 38.5 cm
(15⅛ in.)

29
MEASURING CUPS

Limestone
KhQ 1036, KhQ 1604
First century C.E.
Cup A: Height 7.5 cm
(3 in.), diameter 8 cm
(3⅛ in.)
Cup B: Height 12.8 cm
(5 in.), diameter 19.4 cm
(7½ in.)

Cylindrical cups of this type, ranging in height between 5 and 15 centimeters, are frequently found in sites of the Second Temple period. It is believed that their capacities correspond to the dry and liquid measures mentioned in the Mishnah.

These vessels were pared with a knife or adze, and their surface was left unsmoothed. The vertical handles rule out the possibility that they might have been produced on a rotating lathe.

WOODEN ARTIFACTS

30
BOWL
52.40
First century B.C.E.
Height 4.9 cm (1¹⁵⁄₁₆ in.), diameter 26 cm (10¼ in.)

Wooden artifacts are rare finds in the material culture of the ancient Near East, and few specimens from the Roman period have survived. Therefore, the considerable quantity of organic finds coming from the Judean Desert is an exceptional occurrence. Because of the unusually arid climatic conditions, many wooden objects—bowls, boxes, mirror frames, and combs—were retrieved. Their fine state of preservation facilitates the study of ancient woodworking techniques.

This deep bowl has a flat base, expertly turned on a lathe. Several concentric circles are incised on the base, and the rim of the bowl is rounded. Most of the wooden objects found in the Qumran area are of *acacia tortilis,* a tree prevalent in the southern wadis (valleys) of Israel.

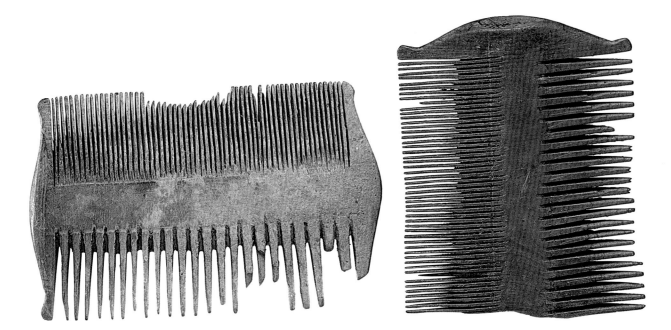

Similar to most of the ancient combs, these boxwood combs are two-sided. One side has closely spaced teeth for straightening the hair, and the opposite side provides more teeth—for delousing.

31
COMBS
Boxwood
52.3, 52.3a
Comb A: Length 6 cm
(2⅜ in.), width 9.5 cm
(3¾ in.)
Comb B: Length 6.3 cm
(2½ in.), width 8 cm
(3⅛ in.)

The Judean Desert has yielded a fair number of leather objects, permitting study of ancient tanning techniques. Water skins, large bags, pouches, purses, sandals, and garments have been found in the varied desert sites.

The majority of leather objects are of sheepskin. A few pieces, particularly those used as patches, are of goatskin and calfskin. The skins were vegetable tanned, mostly with gall and pomegranates. Most of the items shown date from the first century B.C.E. to the first century C.E.

Shown here are sandal soles of the *soleae* type. Intact sandals similar to these were found at Masada and in the Cave of Letters, all in the same region, although representing a range of several centuries.

These soles are made up of three layers of leather secured with leather bindings. Through slits situated near the heel, tabs entered the upper sole. The upper part of each tab was pierced by two vertical slits through which the main strap was threaded. The two ends of the main strap were then threaded into a slit on the upper part of the sandal, near the toe, where they were tied, holding the foot onto the sole.

32
SANDAL
Length 22 cm (8⅝ in.),
width 6.8 cm (2⅝ in.)

33
SANDAL
Length 21 cm (8¼ in.),
width 5.5 cm (2⅛ in.)

LEATHER SCROLL FASTENERS

34
TABS
Length 1.7–2.7 cm
(¹¹⁄₁₆–1¹⁄₁₆ in.), width
1.4–3.3 cm (⁹⁄₁₆–1⁵⁄₁₆ in.)

35
THONGS
Length 7–30 cm
(2¾–11¾ in.), width
0.3–0.8 cm (⅛–⁵⁄₁₆ in.)

The tabs and thongs shown here were most likely used to bind and secure individual scrolls. The fastening is thought to consist of a slotted tab folded over the edge of the scroll (see catalog no. 2) with a thong inserted through its slot. The thong could be tightened and then wound around the scroll. The fasteners were generally made of leather and were prepared in different sizes. The leather thongs may have also been used in the making of phylacteries. (See the related diagram on page 139.)

Reference
Carswell, J. "Fastenings on the Qumrân Manuscripts." In *Qumrân Grotte 4: II. Discoveries in the Judaean Desert, VI*, pp. 23–28 and plates. Oxford, 1977.

36
Phylactery Cases

Leather

4Q Phyl cases 1008

Case A: Length 3.2 cm (1¼ in.), width 1 cm (⅜ in.)

Case B: Length 2.2 cm (⅞ in.), width 1.2 cm (½ in.)

Case C: Length 2 cm (¾ in.), width 1 cm (⅜ in.)

Case D: Length 2.3 cm (⅞ in.), width 2.6 cm (1 in.)

Case E: Length 1.3 cm (½ in.), width 2.1 cm (¹³⁄₁₆ in.)

Case A

This phylactery case has two parts, stitched together. It is a four-compartment type case, worn on the head. Each compartment held a minute roll. Cases C, D, and E are similar to this four-compartment case.

Case B

Worn on the arm, this case has only one compartment. It is formed of a single piece of leather folded in two, with one half deeply stamped out to contain a minute roll. A fine leather thong was inserted at the middle, and the halves were folded over and stitched together.

Reference

Barthélemy, D., and J. T. Milik. *Qumran Cave I*. Discoveries in the Judaean Desert, I, p. 7. Oxford, 1955.

A
B
C

D
E

The textiles here are two out of scores of pieces collected together with scrolls and other objects from the floor of Qumran Cave 1 in the spring of 1949. The textiles were examined at the H. M. Norfolk Flax Establishment in England, and the material was identified as linen. A total of seventy-seven pieces, plain and decorated, were cataloged and described by the renowned textile expert Grace M. Crowfoot, on whose report the following description is based.

All of the pieces appear to have come from small cloths, definitely shaped and sewn. The full measurements of the cloths vary between 57 by 50 centimeters (the largest) and 27 by 23 centimeters (the smallest). They usually have one or two cut edges, hinting that the original loom-woven cloth was larger and wider. These edges were rolled and whipped with a single or double thread. The yarn used in the cloth is all S-spun (the direction of the fiber twist forming an S shape); two-ply thread was sometimes used for sewing. The spinning is fairly good, the warp usually harder and more even than the weft. The linen is generally of fair quality; the highest counts recorded are 18 by 18 and 20 by 16 threads per centimeter, while the lowest are 10 by 8 threads per centimeter. It seems, however, that the weavers were aiming at an even linen weave.

Several cloths have a corded starting border, such as catalog no. 37. It is formed by two groups of threads twined through the warp loops. The warp threads were crossed before the weave started. These details indicate the use of a somewhat primitive loom: possibly the warp-weighted loom, or the two-beamed vertical loom. The quality of both thread and cloth seems to indicate that the linen is a local product.

The only form of colored decoration, although rare, is blue lines, usually two, of indigo-dyed linen threads in the weft. The majority of the cloths are plain, however, some with simple or somewhat more elaborate fringe and with or without an open space. The practice of leaving an open space at one or both ends of a cloth is an ancient tradition and here may have served as a sole ornament: in antiquity decorative bands were usually made with dyed wool because of the extreme difficulty of dying linen; however, this is nonexistent here, probably as a result of the biblical prohibition of *sha'atnez*—the mixing of wool and linen.

It seems probable that all of the cloths from Qumran are linked in one way or another with the scrolls. Some of them were certainly scroll wrappers; the remains of one scroll was found wrapped in a small square of linen. Other cloths, found folded into pads, may have formed a packing for worn-out scrolls inside the jars. Still other pieces—with corners twisted or tied round with linen cord (catalog no. 38)—were probably protective covers, tied over the jar tops.

The materials used as scroll wrappers in the ancient world seem to have varied. The Mishnah, referring to wrappers for the scrolls of the Law, relates: "Handkerchiefs, wrappers for scrolls [of the Law] and bath towels do not come under the law of Diverse Kinds. But R. Eliezer forbids them [if they have in them wool and linen]" (Kil. 9.3). From this it may be inferred that they were usually of linen alone.

Scroll wrappers, when old and worn out, were destined to be deposited together with sacred books in a *genizah* (a storehouse for discarded Hebrew writings and ritual articles). When the *genizah* was too full, the contents were appropriately buried in the cemetery.

It seems reasonable that the majority of the cloths at Qumran were used as scroll wrappers. The wrapped scrolls may have been concealed in a cave at a time of national panic. The concealment also may have constituted the burial of the contents of a *genizah*. The condition of the cloths would coincide with either suggestion.

It is interesting to note that the textiles, of both wool and linen, found at the Murabba'at Cave and in the Cave of Letters, also in the Dead Sea area, are of much greater variety and are parts of garments—tunics, mantles, belts, and kerchiefs, as well as spreads, sacks, nets, and more.

Tamar Schick

Reference
Crowfoot, G. M. "The Linen Textiles." In *Qumran Cave 1*. Discoveries in the Judaean Desert, I, pp. 18–38. Oxford, 1955.

37
LINEN CLOTH
7Q, cloth 30
Length 35.5 cm (13⅞ in.),
width 24 cm (9⅜ in.)
Counts: 14 × 14, 13 × 13,
and in one place 16 × 14
threads per cm

This cloth has edges cut along three sides, rolled and oversewn with a single thread; the fourth edge is a corded starting border in twining technique, followed by a woven strip and an open unwoven space. It was found folded into a pad and was probably used as packing for discarded scrolls.

Reference

Barthélemy, D., and J. T. Milik. *Qumran Cave I*. Discoveries in the Judaean Desert, I, pp. 33–34. Oxford, 1955.

The edges of this cloth are cut, rolled, and whipped on two opposite sides with single thread; on the other two, double thread was used. Two corners are twisted, and the third has a piece of string knotting it, indicating its probable use as a cover for a scroll jar.

Reference

Barthélemy, D., and J. T. Milik. *Qumran Cave I*. Discoveries in the Judaean Desert, I, p. 31. Oxford, 1955.

38
LINEN CLOTH
1Q, cloth 15
Length 29 cm
(11⁵⁄16 in.), width 25 cm
(9¾ in.)
Counts: 17 × 13 threads per cm

Basketry, together with cordage, represents a major type of perishable material retrieved in the arid part of Israel. The basketry fragments on display are made of date palm leaves, a material convenient for making baskets and mats. The technique used is a type of plaiting that was popular during Roman times and remained in favor through the following centuries; a variant is still used in the Near East today.

Because of the exceptional conditions inside caves in the Dead Sea region, several baskets and mats of plaited weave survived intact. Their survival permitted the reconstruction of the Qumran plaited basket, made of a single braid (*zefira* in Mishnaic terms) composed of several elements (*qala'ot*) and spiraling from base to rim. The coiled braid was not sewn together; instead, successive courses were joined around cords as the weaving progressed. In a complete basket the cords are not visible, but they form horizontal ridges and a ribbed texture. Each basket had two arched handles made of palm-fiber rope. Much ingenuity is displayed by the way in which they were attached to the rims: by passing reinforcing cords through the plaited body of the basket.

Basketware was probably very common, as it is to this day, in varied household activities. However, in times of need, baskets and mats also served for collecting and wrapping the bones and skulls of the dead.

Tamar Schick

39
BASKET FRAGMENTS
Palm leaves
11Q
Fragment A:
Length 26 cm (10⅛ in.),
width 16.5 cm (6½ in.).
Three courses preserved
Fragment B:
Length 21.2 cm (8¼ in.),
width 19.5 cm (7⅝ in.).
Four courses preserved
Technique: Braid of 13
elements in 2/2 twill
plaiting

A   B–D

CORDAGE

The cordage on display represents items of varying thickness and use. The raw materials include palm leaves, palm fibers, and rushes. Fragment A probably represents a ridge or reinforcing cord. B–D are heavier cords and might have been used in packing and tying bundles and water skins. Fragment E is a detached handle. The freestanding end of a handle cord that links the handle to the basket can be discerned in one of the loops.

E

40A

CORD

Palm leaves

1Q and 2Q

Diameter 3 mm (⅛ in.)

Technique: 2-ply cable,

final twist in S *direction*

(z2s)

40B–D

ROPES

Palm leaves and

undetermined rushes

Diameter 7–10 mm

(¼–⁷⁄₁₆ in.)

Technique: 3 ply-cable,

final twist Z *(s3z);*

one rope has an

overhand knot

40E

HEAVY ROPE

Diameter 15–20 mm

(⅝–1³⁄₁₆ in.)

Technique: Compound

3-ply cable, final twist Z

(z3s3z)

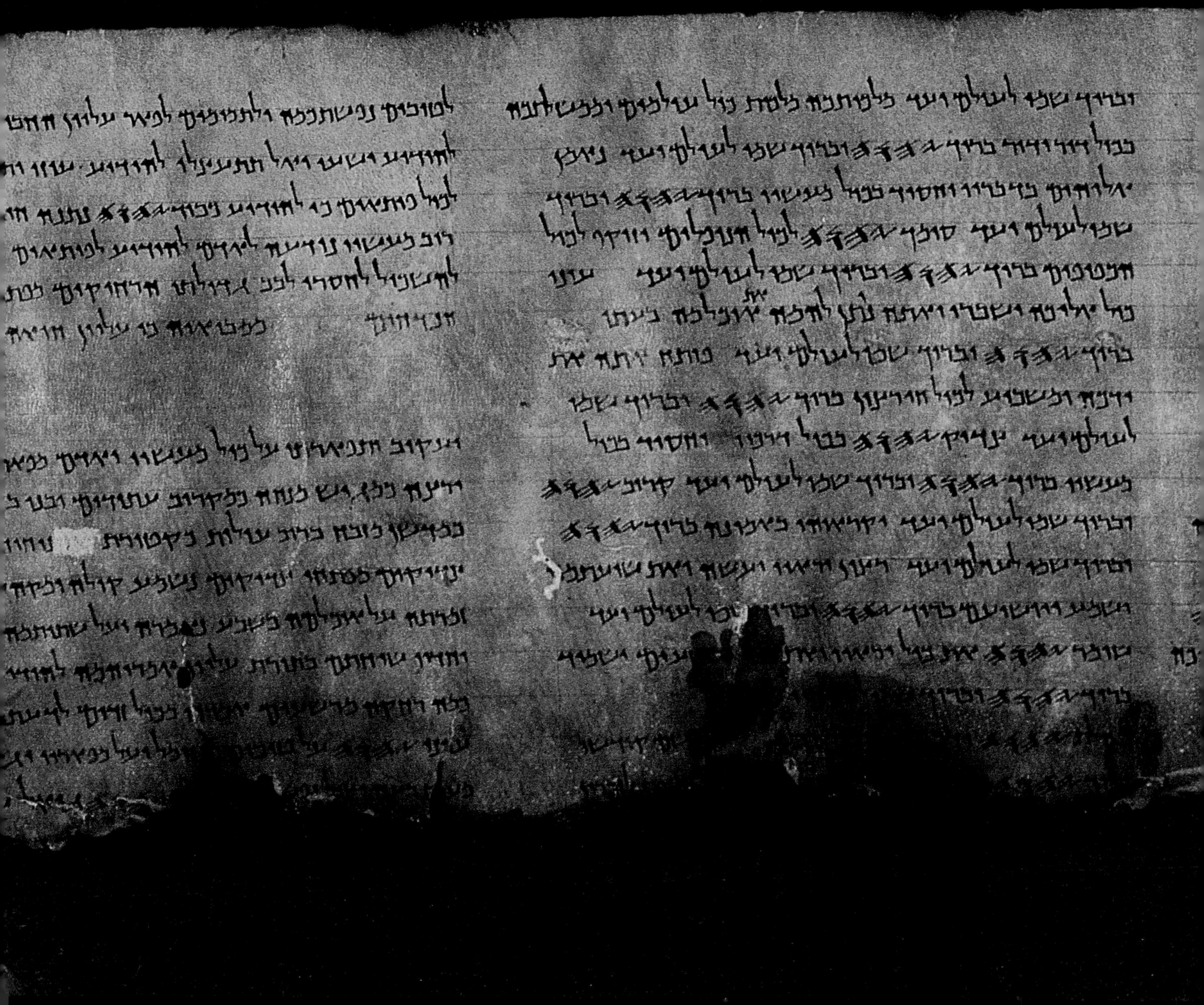

APPENDIX

The Paleo-Hebrew and Jewish Scripts

Ada Yardeni

The ancient Hebrew script, also known as the paleo-Hebrew script, is one of the offshoots of the Phoenician script. It was the exclusive Hebrew script of the First Temple period from about 850 to 586 B.C.E., in both the Judean and the Israelite kingdoms.

In the wake of the destruction of the First Temple (586 B.C.E.) and the ensuing exile, Hebrew lost its prominent, singular status in favor of Aramaic, which had become the official language of the Persian empire. In the Post-Exilic period, in the Diaspora and in Judea as well, the cursive Aramaic script gradually replaced the ancient Hebrew script for secular writing as well as for holy scriptures. (Jewish tradition maintains that Ezra the Scribe established that custom on returning from the Babylonian exile.) The paleo-Hebrew script, however, was not completely abandoned. Although of limited use, it apparently held a high nationalistic and religious status and was used particularly in priestly circles, as well as in times of nationalistic strife or revival. The paleo-Hebrew script appears on a variety of materials: stone, pottery, coins, and papyrus. However, the major finds in this script from the late Second Temple period are from Qumran. Paleo-Hebrew characters are used for about a dozen biblical scrolls and, interestingly, are employed for writing the Tetragrammaton, the four-letter divine name (see catalog no. 4), and occasionally in manuscripts otherwise written in the Jewish script.

The major changes that occurred in the paleo-Hebrew script were the leveling of the height of the letters of the alphabet (the Jewish script underwent a similar process) and changes in the stance of the letters. Of chronological significance are the changes in the length of the downstrokes and in the inclination of the letters toward the ensuing letters. However, a proper cursive style did not evolve in paleo-Hebrew script, possibly because of its limited use.

Of special interest is the Leviticus Scroll from Qumran (catalog no. 3), written in the paleo-Hebrew script. The Leviticus fragments were dated on paleographical grounds (their script resembling the script on Hasmonean coins) to the late second–early first century B.C.E. The almost uniform direction of the downstrokes, sloping to the left, indicates an experienced, rapid, and rhythmic hand. A version of the paleo-Hebrew script is used today by the Samaritans.

The Jewish script is one of the offshoots of the late formal Aramaic cursive script. It emerged when the latter split into local scripts following the fall of the Persian empire in the second half of the fourth century B.C.E.

A group of dated documents, the latest from 335 B.C.E., found at Wadi Daliyeh along the Jordan Valley, is in the late Aramaic script. It bears affinity with the script of the earliest Qumran scroll fragments (4QSam[b]), which may be regarded as a link between the Aramaic and the Jewish scripts. Certain late Aramaic letter forms prevail in documents written in early Jewish script (such as the looped *alef* and the looped *tav,* the final *lamed,* and the final *nun,* etc.).

The earliest dated document in the Jewish script is from Wadi Murabba'at, dated to the second year of the emperor Nero (55/56 C.E.). Because no Qumran document yet published bears an explicit date, Qumran scholars must rely on historical, archaeological, and paleographical data. Thus, the earliest documents from Qumran have been dated to the late third or early second century B.C.E. Formal development of the letters is reflected, for example, in the straightening of the curved strokes resulting in the formation of angular joins, which give the Jewish bookhand its square appearance. Another characteristic is the regularity of the writing, which is a result of the suspension of the letters on horizontal guidelines (not attested in Aramaic documents written in ink). At this early stage of independent development, the letters in the Jewish script were not yet adorned with ornamental additions, except for the inherited serifs in several letters (for example, *dalet, kaf, mem, qof,* and *resh*). The distinction between thick horizontal and thin vertical strokes, characteristic of the late Aramaic scripts, is still evidenced in the earliest documents from Qumran—and occasionally even in later documents—but is not typical of the Jewish script.

Three main periods in the development of the Jewish script are distinguished: the Hasmonean period (167–30 B.C.E.), the Herodian period (30 B.C.E.– 70 C.E.), and the post-Herodian period (70–135 C.E.). The majority of Qumran documents belong to the first two periods, although some earlier fragments are available. The variety of handwritings testifies to the activity of scores of scribes. It is reasonable, therefore, to believe that a great many documents found in the caves of Qumran came from other places.

Fragments of the Book of Enoch (catalog no. 9) include fine examples of early Hasmonean script. The Prayer for King Jonathan (Alexander Jannaeus, 103–76 B.C.E.) (catalog no. 2), dated to the first quarter of the first century B.C.E., exhibits a variety of letter forms in bookhand as well as semicursive and cursive hands (for example, three forms of the letter *mem*).

A significant increase in ornamental elements in the letters—in the form of independent additional strokes—is evidenced in the Herodian period, together with the leveling of the height of the letters. Examples of the Herodian script here include the Psalms Scroll (catalog no. 4) and the Hosea Commentary (no. 5). It also is characterized by the crystallization of different script styles, such as the calligraphic bookhand (later to develop into the ornamental script style used for Torah scrolls), and the standard cursive script style that prevailed in Judea during the late Herodian and the post-Herodian periods. It went out of use at the end of the Bar Kokhba revolt (135 C.E.). This cursive style served for official as well as literary documents: an early form appears, for example, in one of the manuscripts of Enoch from Qumran (4Q212), and its later forms are attested on ossuaries and inscriptions from the Herodian period, on ostraca from Masada dating to the end of the Herodian period, and in documents from the late first and early second centuries C.E. The Jewish bookhand continued to exist and developed many script styles in widely dispersed Jewish communities. The Hebrew script used today is its modern descendant.

	PALEO- HEBREW 8th century B.C.E.	JEWISH SCRIPT Temple Scroll	ORIENTAL* 9th–10th centuries	SEFARDI 13th–15th centuries	ASHKENAZI 14th–15th centuries
alef					
bet					
gimmel					
dalet					
he					
vav					
zayin					
ḥet					
tet					
yod					
kaf					
final kaf					
lamed					

STYLES OF HEBREW SCRIPT

PALEO-HEBREW	JEWISH SCRIPT	ORIENTAL*	SEFARDI	ASHKENAZI	
8th century B.C.E.	Temple Scroll	9th–10th centuries	13th–15th centuries	14th–15th centuries	
מ	מ	מ	מ	מ	mem
	ם	ם	ם	ם	final mem
נ	נ	נ	נ	נ	nun
	ן	ן	ן	ן	final nun
	ס	ס	ס	ס	samech
☉	ע	ע	ע	ע	ayin
⊃	פ	פ	פ	פ	peh
	ף	ף	ף	ף	final peh (feh)
	צ	צ	צ	צ	ẓade
	ץ	ץ	ץ	ץ	final ẓade
ף	ק	ק	ק	ק	qof
ף	ר	ר	ר	ר	resh
ש	ש	ש	ש	ש	shin
×	ת	ת	ת	ת	tav

* Includes handwritings used in the Near East and North Africa

Preservation of the Scroll Fragments

Esther Boyd-Alkalay

The constant, arid climate of the Dead Sea region, which is 1,300 feet below sea level, probably contributed most to the preservation of the scrolls over two millennia. The transfer of the documents to Jerusalem, beginning in 1947, rendered them vulnerable to damage. Of particular significance is the drastic change in climatic conditions, as Jerusalem is 2,400 feet above sea level—considerably higher than the Judean Desert site where the scrolls were discovered.

When these artifacts were brought to Jerusalem, they were handled inappropriately in an uncontrolled environment. Cellophane tape was used to join fragments and cover cracks, causing irreversible damage. The scrolls were moistened and flattened loosely between plates of window glass and sealed with adhesive tape. The aging of the adhesives and the pressure of the glass caused the scroll edges to gelatinize and the skins themselves to darken in some cases to such an extent that the texts are no longer legible.

In the 1970s a team of conservators from the Israel Museum began to treat the damaged scroll fragments: they removed the cellophane tape and some of the stains, reinforced the fragments, and replaced the glass plates with cardboard. The severe degree of deterioration, however, called for more urgent steps.

In 1991 the Israel Antiquities Authority established a climate-controlled storeroom and laboratory in the Rockefeller Museum Building in Jerusalem for the conservation and preservation of the scrolls. Four full-time conservators are currently working to preserve them from further decay.

While preparing the scrolls for exhibition, a new housing system was devised. The fragments are being sewn between two layers of Stabiltex (polyester net) stretched in acid-free mounts and enclosed in a frame made of polycarbonate plates. Each fragment is photographed, mapped, and detailed in a condition report.

The most time-consuming task, however, remains the removal of the cellophane tape applied soon after the discovery. Water-based adhesives are used to loosen the tape, after which a dry poulticing material is applied to remove the tape residues and stains. Once the remains are removed, oils and other stains are treated and the scroll versos are reinforced wherever necessary. Because this operation cannot be standardized, each of the thousands of extant fragments requires individual consideration.

Unfortunately, the scrolls cannot be prevented from aging naturally. We are, however, trying to slow the aging process with minimum intervention. Although the preservation of the Dead Sea Scrolls is an extremely lengthy, painstaking, and costly task, they represent a universal cultural heritage that is our duty to safeguard and preserve for future generations.

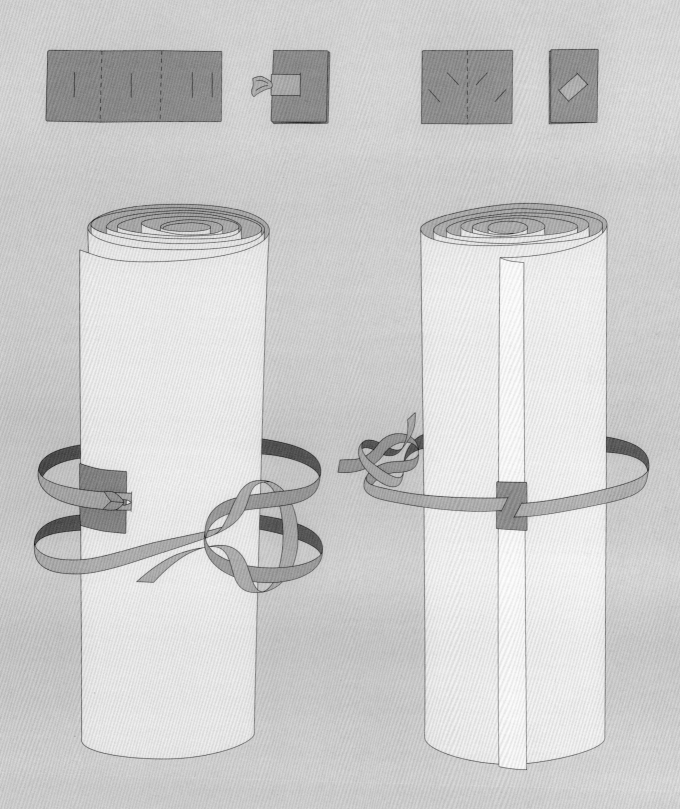

RECONSTRUCTION OF SCROLLS SHOWING
TWO TYPES OF FASTENINGS AND REINFORCING TABS

EPILOGUE: PUBLICATION OF THE DEAD SEA SCROLLS

Emanuel Tov

Tens of thousands of inscribed fragments of parchment—pieces from almost one thousand compositions, mainly literary documents—were found in the Judean Desert, particularly the Qumran area, beginning in 1947. The majority, fragments of some eight hundred documents, come from the caves around Qumran, while remnants of more than 150 documents and compositions were found in other locations in the Judean Desert—for example, Naḥal Ḥever, Wadi Murabbaʿat, Naḥal Ṣeʿelim, and Masada. Several compositions were preserved in large scrolls, while others are single-page documents.

Well-preserved texts included long ones such as the Isaiah Scroll from Cave 1 (twenty-four feet) and the Temple Scroll from Cave 11 (twenty-nine feet). Most of the compositions, however, are fragmentary. The pieces were sorted into hundreds of groups, and, like working jigsaw puzzles, scholars attempted to assemble comprehensible texts. The tiny fragment of Chronicles (4Q118) represents all that has been preserved of the sixty-five biblical chapters of 1–2 Chronicles. But a more difficult and more representative case is that of the pseudo-Ezekiel literature, for which there are tens of fragments representing an unknown percentage of an unknown number of compositions.

The texts from the Judean Desert include more than 200 scrolls of biblical compositions, several hundred varied literary compositions, and a limited number of nonliterary documents. These documents, in Hebrew, Aramaic, Nabatean, and Greek, are of crucial importance for the study of the early exegesis of the Bible, its textual transmission, and the Hebrew and Aramaic languages, as well as the literature and the history of ideas of the Second Temple period.

Full publication of this complex corpus of documents has taken longer than was envisaged by the small team assigned in the 1950s to publish the newly found texts. Publication includes identification; decipherment; transcription; reconstruction; annotation on matters of paleography, text, and meaning; dating; and, in the case of the nonbiblical texts, translation as well. All of these elements, accompanied by facsimiles of the texts, are included in the official edition, published by Oxford University Press: Discoveries in the Judaean Desert (DJD). Volume XXVII has recently appeared; another thirteen volumes are scheduled to be published in this series, along with an index volume and a complete concordance. Sixty scholars from nine countries, representing North America, Israel, and Europe—expanded from the original eight persons in the 1950s—are engaged in this project.

In addition, photographs of all fragments have been available since 1993 in a microfiche edition by E. Tov with the collaboration of S. J. Pfann: *The Dead Sea Scrolls on Microfiche: A Comprehensive Facsimile Edition of the Texts from the Judaean Desert.*

Official Series

Discoveries in the Judaean Desert. Oxford: Clarendon Press, Oxford University Press, 1955– .

Vol. I: Barthélemy, D., and J. T. Milik. *Qumran Cave I*. 1955.

Vol. II: Benoit, P., J. T. Milik, and R. de Vaux. *Les Grottes de Murabbaʿât*. 1961.

Vol. III: Baillet, M., J. T. Milik, and R. de Vaux. *Les 'Petites Grottes' de Qumran*. 1962.

Vol. IV: Sanders, J. A. *The Psalms Scroll of Qumrân Cave 11 (11QPsᵃ)*. 1965.

Vol. V: Allegro, J. M. *Qumrân Cave 4: I (4Q158–4Q186)*. 1968.

Vol. VI: De Vaux, R., and J. T. Milik. *Qumrân Grotte 4: II (Archéologie et 4Q128–4Q157)*. 1977.

Vol. VII: Baillet, M. *Qumrân Grotte 4: III (4Q482–4Q520)*. 1982.

Vol. VIII: Tov, E. *The Greek Minor Prophets Scroll from Naḥal Ḥever (8ḤevXIIgr) (The Seiyâl Collection I)*. 1990.

Vol. IX: Skehan, P., E. Ulrich, and J. Sanderson, with a contribution by P. J. Parsons. *Qumran Cave 4: IV. Palaeo-Hebrew and Greek Biblical Manuscripts*. 1992.

Vol. X: Qimron, E., and J. Strugnell. *Qumran Cave 4: V. Miqṣat Maʿase ha-Torah*. 1994.

Vol. XI: Eshel, E., et al. *Qumran Cave 4: VI. Poetical and Liturgical Texts, Part 1*. 1998.

Vol. XII: Ulrich, E., and F. M. Cross, eds. *Qumran Cave 4: VII. Genesis to Numbers*. 1994.

Vol. XIII: Attridge, H., et al. *Qumran Cave 4: VIII. Parabiblical Texts, Part 1*. 1994.

Vol. XIV: Ulrich, E., and F. M. Cross, eds. *Qumran Cave 4: IX. Deuteronomy, Joshua, Judges, Kings*. 1995.

Vol. XV: Ulrich, E., ed. *Qumran Cave 4: X. The Prophets*. 1997.

Vol. XVIII: Baumgarten, J. M. *Qumran Cave 4: XIII. The Damascus Document (4Q266–273)*. 1996.

Vol. XIX: Broshi, M., et al. *Qumran Cave 4: XIV. Parabiblical Texts, Part 2*. 1995.

Vol. XX: Elgvin, T., et al. *Qumran Cave 4: XV. Sapiential Texts, Part 1*. 1997.

Vol. XXII: Brooke, G., et al. *Qumran Cave 4: XVII. Parabiblical Texts, Part 3*. 1996.

Vol. XXIII: García Martínez, F., E.J.C. Tigchelaar, and A. S. van der Woude. *Qumran Cave 11: II. 11Q2–18, 11Q20–30*. 1998.

Vol. XXIV: Leith, M.J.W. *The Wadi Daliyeh Seal Impressions*. 1997.

Vol. XXV: Puech, E. *Qumran Cave 4: XVII. Textes Hébreux*. 1998.

Vol. XXVI: Alexander, P., and G. Vermes. *Qumran Cave 4: XIX. 4Q Serekh Ha-Yahad and Two Related Texts*. 1998.

Vol. XXVII: Cotton, H. M., and A. Yardeni. *Aramaic, Hebrew, and Greek Documentary Texts from Nahal Hever and other Sites (The Seiyal Collection II)*. 1997.

Selected Readings

GENERAL SOURCES

Boccaccini, G. *Beyond the Essene Hypothesis: The Parting of the Ways between Qumran and Enochic Judaism.* Grand Rapids: Eerdmans, 1998.

Collins, J. *Apocalypticism in the Dead Sea Scrolls.* London: Rutledge, 1997.

Charlesworth, J. H., ed. *Jesus and the Dead Sea Scrolls.* New York: Crossroads, 1992.

Cross, F. M. "The Development of the Jewish Scripts." In *The Bible and the Ancient Near East: Essays in Honor of William Foxwell Albright.* Edited by G. E. Wright. Rev. ed. Garden City, N.Y.: Doubleday, 1995.

De Vaux, R. *Archaeology and the Dead Sea Scrolls.* Oxford: Oxford University Press, 1973.

Dimant, D., and U. Rappaport, eds. *The Ancient Library of Qumran.* 3rd ed. Minneapolis: Fortress Press, 1996.

———. *The Dead Sea Scrolls: Forty Years of Research.* Leiden: Brill, 1992.

Fitzmyer, J. *Responses to 101 Questions on the Dead Sea Scrolls.* New York: Paulist Press, 1992.

Flint, P. W., and J. C. Vanderkam, eds. *The Dead Sea Scrolls After Fifty Years: A Comprehensive Assessment.* Leiden: Brill, 1998.

García-Martínez, F. *The Dead Sea Scrolls Translated.* 2nd ed. Leiden: Brill, 1997.

Kugel, J. *The Bible as It Was.* Cambridge: Harvard University Press, 1995.

Schechter, S. *Documents of Jewish Sectaries.* 1910. Reprint. Library of Biblical Studies. New York: KTAV Press, 1970.

Schiffman, L. H. *Reclaiming the Dead Sea Scrolls.* Philadelphia: Jewish Publication Society, 1996.

Shanks, H., ed. *Understanding the Dead Sea Scrolls: A Reader from the Biblical Archaeological Review.* New York: Random House, 1992.

Stegemann, H. *The Library of Qumran: On the Essenes, Qumran, John the Baptist and Jesus.* Grand Rapids: Eerdmans, 1998.

Ulrich, Eugene. *The Dead Sea Scrolls and the Origin of the Bible.* Grand Rapids: Eerdmans, 1999.

Vanderkam, J. *Calendars in the Dead Sea Scrolls: Measuring Time.* London: Routledge, 1998.

———. *The Dead Sea Scrolls Today.* Grand Rapids: Eerdmans, 1994.

Vermes, G. *The Complete Dead Sea Scrolls in English.* 5th ed. New York: Penguin, 1997.

Transcriptions, Reproductions, and Reconstructions

The Dead Sea Scrolls on Microfiche: A Comprehensive Facsimile Edition of the Texts from the Judaean Desert. Edited by E. Tov. Printed catalog by S. Reed. Israel Antiquities Authority. Leiden: E. J. Brill, 1993.

A Facsimile Edition of the Dead Sea Scrolls. Prepared with an introduction and index by R. Eisenman and J. Robinson. 2 vols. Washington, D.C.: Biblical Archaeology Society, 1991.

A Preliminary Edition of the Unpublished Dead Sea Scrolls: The Hebrew and Aramaic Texts from Cave Four. Reconstructed and edited by B. Wacholder and M. Abegg. 2 fascs. Washington, D.C.: Biblical Archaeology Society, 1991–92.

The Scroll of the War of the Sons of Light Against the Sons of Darkness. Edited by Y. Yadin. Translated by B. and C. Rabin. Oxford: Oxford University Press, 1962.

Scrolls from Qumrân Cave I: The Great Isaiah Scroll, the Order of the Community, the Pesher to Habakkuk. Photographs by J. Trever. Jerusalem: Albright Institute of Archaeological Research and the Shrine of the Book, 1972.

The Temple Scroll. Edited by Y. Yadin. 3 vols. Jerusalem: Israel Exploration Society, 1977–83.

Michael W. Grunberger
James L. Phillips
Ayala Sussmann

For this exhibition and catalog, kind advice was extended to us by a number of colleagues, all specialists in their fields. We are particularly indebted to Professors J. Greenfield, E. Tov, M. Broshi, and E. Qimron for reading our manuscript or parts thereof and offering information and advice.

We would like to extend our thanks to our colleagues at the Israel Antiquities Authority, without whom this exhibition would not have been possible: Jacob Fisch, who coordinated the logistics of the exhibit; Sarah Ben Arieh, Pnina Shor, Hava Katz, Esther Boyd-Alkalay, and Tamar Schick; and Lena Liebman, Tanya Bitter, and Olga Navitzky, whose treatment of the scrolls and steps taken toward their preservation allowed the exhibition.

The studio photographs are chiefly the work of Yoram Lehman, Tsila Sagiv, and Clara Amit. Area photographs are by Duby Tal and David Harris.

We thank them all for their efforts.

Ayala Sussmann and Ruth Peled, Israel Antiquities Authority

AUTHORS' ACKNOWL-EDGMENTS

It was clear from the inception of the exhibition that to complete it in the time allotted we would need the generous and timely assistance of a multitude of experts in Israel and the United States. First and foremost we are grateful to Amir Drori, director of the Israel Antiquities Authority, whose idea it was to mount a traveling exhibition featuring these scrolls. His aspiration could not have been realized without the steadfast support of Librarian of Congress James H. Billington, whose keen interest in the project ensured its successful completion.

At the Library of Congress, Irene Chambers, director of the interpretive programs office, provided overall direction for this exhibition, including its national program. Doris A. Hamburg, acting conservation officer, developed the conservation specifications for the exhibition objects, designed the housings used to mount the scrolls, oversaw the shipping and packing of the objects, and prepared the interim and final condition reports. Annlinn Krug Grossman, conservator, fabricated all the scroll housings, and Margaret R. Brown, senior conservator, compiled the condition notebooks and provided additional conservation support. Tambra Johnson, registrar, planned and implemented the complex set of travel arrangements for couriers and cargo from Jerusalem to Washington, New York, and San Francisco and back to Jerusalem and prepared the various applications required to organize an international traveling exhibition. Norma Baker, director of the development office, served as liaison with the exhibition's sponsors and venues. John Kominski, general counsel, was instrumental in formulating the various agreements that support this international loan exhibition.

We are pleased to acknowledge the assistance of colleagues in Israel and the

United States who have made this complicated undertaking possible. At the Israel Antiquities Authority we thank Jacob Fisch, director of marketing; Ruth Peled, chief curator; Tamar Schick, curator of organic materials; and Ayala Sussmann, director of publications. At the New York Public Library we are grateful for the cooperation of Leonard S. Gold, Dorot chief librarian of the Jewish Division; Susan F. Saidenberg, manager of exhibitions; Jean Mihich, registrar; Lou Storey, exhibitions designer and installation specialist; and Bonnie Rosenblum, manager of corporate relations. At the Fine Arts Museums of San Francisco we thank Melissa Leventon, acting curator of textiles, and Harry S. Parker III, director, for their participation and helpful suggestions.

Dana Pratt, director of the publishing office, played a key role in enabling this catalog to be published. We are indebted to Diane Maddex, president of Archetype Press, who oversaw and coordinated all aspects of this publication, and Robert L. Wiser, art director, who was responsible for its design.

We are deeply grateful to Mark E. Talisman, president of Project Judaica Foundation, whose early and continuing support for this exhibition enabled the participants to begin the critical planning and conservation tasks that permitted it to traverse the gulf between dream and reality—in record time.

Michael W. Grunberger, Library of Congress, 1993

CONTRIBUTORS

Donald T. Ariel is curator of numismatics, Israel Antiquities Authority.

Esther Boyd-Alkalay is restoration consultant, Israel Antiquities Authority.

Michael W. Grunberger is head of the Hebraic Section, Library of Congress.

Ruth Peled is chief curator, Israel Antiquities Authority, and co-curator of *Scrolls from the Dead Sea.*

James L. Phillips is adjunct curator of Near Eastern and North African archaeology, the Field Museum, and professor of anthropology, University of Illinois, Chicago.

Tamar Schick is curator of organic materials, Israel Antiquities Authority.

Ayala Sussmann is director of publications, Israel Antiquities Authority, and co-curator of *Scrolls from the Dead Sea.*

Emanuel Tov is professor of biblical literature, Hebrew University of Jerusalem, and editor-in-chief of the Dead Sea Scrolls Publication Project, Israel Antiquities Authority.

Ada Yardeni is research fellow in paleography, Hebrew University of Jerusalem.

Unless otherwise indicated, photographs in this catalog have been used with permission of the Israel Antiquities Authority.

Page 1: Scroll fragment featuring commentary *(pesher)* on the biblical verses of Hosea 2:8–14 (catalog no. 5; see pages 46–49). (Israel Antiquities Authority)

Page 13: A conservator with the Israel Antiquities Authority working on one of the scroll fragments. (Israel Antiquities Authority)

Page 28: Qumran and the Dea Sea seen from a scroll cave. (David Harris, Jerusalem)

Page 88: Aerial view of the Qumran ruin. (Duby Tal, Albatross Studio, Tel Aviv)

ILLUSTRATIONS AND CREDITS

Pages 136–37: Chart adapted from "Styles of Hebrew Scripts," *Scribes, Script and Books* by Leila Avrin, pp. 126–27 (Chicago, 1991). Used with permission of the American Library Association.

Page 139: Scroll diagram adapted from "Fastenings on the Qumrân Manuscripts," *Qumrân Grotte 4: II,* Discoveries in the Judaean Desert, VI, pp. 26–27 (Oxford, 1977). Used with permission of Clarendon Press and the Israel Antiquities Authority.

The translation on page 39 is adapted from *Tanakh: A New Translation of the Holy Scriptures According to the Traditional Hebrew Text,* p. 192 (Philadelphia, 1985). Used with permission of the Jewish Publication Society.

The translations on pages 71, 75, and 79 are from G. Vermes, *The Complete Dead Sea Scrolls in English* (New York, 1997). Used with permission of G. Vermes and Penguin Books.

INDEX